ELEMENTARY LINEAR PROGRAMMING

QUANTITATIVE TECHNIQUES FOR ECONOMISTS   A Series Under
the Editorial
Supervision of
E. J. Mishan

RANDOM HOUSE, NEW YORK

ELEMENTARY LINEAR PROGRAMMING

C. D. THROSBY

Macquarie University / Sydney, Australia

FIRST PRINTING

98765432

Copyright © 1970 by Random House, Inc.
All rights reserved under International and Pan-American Copyright Conventions.
Published in the United States by Random House, Inc., New York, and
simultaneously in Canada by Random House of Canada Limited, Toronto.

Library of Congress Catalog Card Number: 79-83356

Manufactured in the United States of America.

INTRODUCTION TO THE SERIES

BY E. J. MISHAN

Since the war, economics has come into a rich mathematical legacy: for most of us, indeed, an *embarras de richesse*. There are not many economists who can take any issue of, say, *Econometrica, The Review of Economic Studies*, or the *International Economic Review*—to say nothing of the more specialized journals on management science or operations research—and read through all of the contributions without difficulty. Those brought up in the older, more literary, tradition find it hard enough to keep abreast of the literature presented even in the less mathematical journals.

The controversy concerning the contribution to be made by mathematics to economic knowledge continues—if not in print, at least verbally. But whatever be the ultimate judgment on this elusive question, it must be recognized that once mathematics has become an accepted currency of the subject, it is hardly possible for the economist ignorant of its uses to maintain his professional status. The nonmathematical economist will not be able to determine at first hand whether or not the contributions of mathematical economics are significant, and unless he learns the language in which their arguments are expressed he cannot know just what his fellow economists are thinking.

The response over the last decade to this growing tendency to employ mathematical techniques for testing economic theorems and solving economic problems has been an increase of mathematical and statistical instruction in the undergraduate curriculum. To meet the needs of the undergraduate, a number of introductory books on mathematical economics have appeared, supplemented by a few on linear programming, input-output, operations research, and game theory. The interests of the mathematical economist, on the other hand, have also been met by a number of books displaying recent advances in the subject and more elegant and general proofs of well-known theorems. There is, however, a very large group who can derive only limited benefit from either the introductory or the advanced works. It includes the greater number of economic journalists and practicing economists as well as those academic economists with otherwise sound professional training yet lacking in the mathematical sophistication necessary to keep abreast of the journal literature, even within their own field of competence. For a member of this large class of academic economists, the ordinary introductory text is either unnecessary or does not go far enough, while obviously the specialized mathematical treatises are beyond his grasp.

The series *Quantitative Techniques for Economists* caters to this group of economists. It aims to produce volumes devoted solely to training the economist in the use of a number mathematical or other technique.

Since there would be differences in the mathematical reach among those comprising this class of economists, it will be our policy to begin each subject at the most elementary level. Yet it is the hope of the editor that the chief aim of the series will be realized and the entire subject treated with a thoroughness that will enable the reader eventually to feel at home with the bulk of the papers using the techniques treated in these volumes.

Two particular features will mark the series. First, the pedagogical method to be employed will be the reverse of that generally employed in the journal literature and even in many textbooks. Among the latter the chief aim is elegance and generality after which, perhaps, instances and special cases are provided. The treatment in this series will instead begin with the simple instances and the special cases, and work gradually toward generalization. In any case, it is by working through simple instances and special cases that people arrive at generalizations—and it is but a vanity among the learned professions that impels academics to write in a manner that is the very reverse of the way they actually reach their conclusions. Secondly, the development of each of the subjects treated will proceed, from the start, through the medium of economic examples. The interest of the reader primarily concerned with economics will be engaged from the start: his time will not be wasted even if he reads only a little way. Roundabout methods may give higher returns for the raw student. But for this group we make provision for immediate if more modest returns. Another obvious advantage of this method of exposition is the strong likelihood of its being able also to advance the substantive economic knowledge of the reader. Certainly the attempt will be made to parallel the elaboration of the technical apparatus with a systematic development of the economics that are, or may be, treated by such techniques.

It goes without saying that there will be many others outside this particular class of readers who may profit from the series. This includes students of other social sciences, business students, managers, and others eager to acquire some competence and facility with mathematical techniques that have application in closely similar problems. Less specialized students and undergraduates will be able to profit from the earlier chapters in several of the treatises, and graduates, it is hoped, will turn to them for a serious treatment of the economics along with the mathematics.

PREFACE

The purpose of this introductory text is to ground the student thoroughly in the ideas of linear programming, the most important technique in the field of mathematical programming. With the increasing availability and use of electronic computers to solve linear programming problems, more and more people wish to understand and use the technique but are deterred by the prospect of working through the tedious mechanical rules involved in the manual solution of programming problems. A novel feature of this text is the sequence in which the subject matter is treated. In the first two parts the reader gradually gains an understanding of the nature of linear programming problems and their solution, without becoming tied down in a mere recitation of rules of thumb. By the end of Part II he will have gained sufficient insight to comprehend the general ways in which linear programming problems are set up, and to interpret the sort of solutions a computer would generate for him. For those who desire a complete treatment of the computational side of the simplex method, Part III covers the algebraic origins of the method and contains an extensive exposition and discussion of the rules for manual computation.

In other words this sequence of contents has a twofold purpose. First, by building up in Parts I and II an understanding of the logic of the steps involved in the simplex method, this book meets the needs of those who will solve linear programming problems exclusively on electronic computers and who do not wish to worry about finer details of computational techniques. Second, it is expected that those who do wish to gain a fuller understanding of computational methods will find Part III very much easier, having been broken in gradually over Parts I and II.

As an expositional device many numerical examples are used which reflect the wide variety of economic problems to which linear programming is applicable. The numbers used in these examples are entirely hypothetical and in many cases unrealistic. We have farmers heaping tons of fertilizer on the soil to produce a few meager bushels of grain; we have a penniless invalid whose optimum daily diet consists of a cabbage and one-half pint of milk; we have industrialists attempting to produce motor fuels from unlikely ingredients; and other such examples. No apology is made for these unrealistic numerical examples; the aim is to point up features of the ideas and techniques under study, rather than to reflect empirical conditions in the real world. In these circumstances, the pursuit of realism can easily become an unnecessary complication.

A rough outline of the contents of this text is given below.

Part I, "Setting Up Simple Linear Programming Problems," covering Chapters 1 through 5, treats maximization and minimization problems concurrently, and develops the fundamental concept of a basic solution. By being shown the way in which variables are introduced into and eliminated from a basis, the reader begins to grasp the iterative nature of the simplex solution procedure.

Part II, "Setting Up More Complex Linear Programming Problems," covers Chapters 6 through 10. After the concept of artificial variables is introduced in Chapter 6, the dual formulations of linear programming problems are discussed in Chapter 7. In this chapter the dual is presented and analyzed in terms of an example in which both primal and dual variables have a concrete economic interpretation. This example simplifies the treatment and facilitates subsequent comprehension of more abstract cases. By the end of Chapter 9 most of the common constraint forms and types of solution have been dealt with; thus the way is paved for an example in Chapter 10 of the interpretation of a typical computer output resulting from the solution of a linear programming problem by electronic computer.

Part III is concerned with "Computational Aspects." Chapter 11 returns to first principles and shows the algebraic derivation of a simplex transformation. As mentioned above, the reader should be readily familiar with the process at this stage, as he should already have acquired an understanding of it from the first two parts. In Chapter 12 the techniques of basis transformation are presented *per se*, related back to the algebraic derivations of Chapter 11, and it is not until Chapter 13 that the question of optimization is reintroduced. After the computation of the simplex with artificial variables is dealt with in Chapter 14, a full collation and summary of the simplex rules appear in Chapter 15. Finally, in Chapter 16, the dual treatment is rounded off and a general algebraic interpretation of the setup of primal and dual problems is given. The fact that this *generalized* interpretative statement does not appear until Chapter 16 is a reflection of the simple expositional orientation of this book.

Exercises at the end of each chapter test the student's progress and extend his appreciation of the subject by introducing him to a range of applications in the linear programming field. The numerical examples used in various chapters of the text (two basic numerical examples are carried through from beginning to end) are closely interrelated with each other and with the exercises. It is hoped that the continuity provided by these recurring examples will tend to unify the treatment as a whole.

A fairly practical outlook has been maintained in considering what subject matter should be included; hence the framework of *theory* surrounding linear programming is dealt with only when it has immediate relevance to the setting up and direct solution of programming *problems*. This approach will also be used in the next volume, *Introduction to Mathematical Programming*, which will cover advanced aspects of the formulation and solution of mathematical programming problems, including sensitivity analysis, parametric programming, and dynamic, stochastic and nonlinear models.

The present volume covers sufficient ground to bring the student to the point of a fairly full understanding of quite complex linear programming problems. Yet it is not intended to serve by itself as a practical manual or recipe book. Application of programming to real-world problems is a process requiring judgment, intuition, ingenuity, and imagination, none of which can be taught.

The form of this book was originally worked out in collaboration with Dr. E. J. Mishan, editor of this series, during a period when the author was on the staff of the London School of Economics. The subsequent translation of form into substance was also carried out under Dr. Mishan's beneficent supervision. The shape of this book owes much to his ideas about the task of the series as a whole, as well as to his detailed editing. However, while placing on record my gratitude to him, I myself assume sole responsibility for errors or shortcomings of whatever sort.

C. D. T.
Sydney, Australia
February 1969

CONTENTS

Contents

SETTING UP SIMPLE LINEAR PROGRAMMING PROBLEMS

PART I

1

A SIMPLE
MAXIMIZATION PROBLEM

1.1 Maximum Constraints

Imagine a farmer who can produce wheat, barley, or some combination of these two crops. Suppose the only factor of production he needs is land. If land is available to the farmer in unlimited quantities, he can produce any amounts of wheat and barley he likes. There is no problem of scarcity of resources in this case.

If, however, the farmer has only, say, 8 acres of land available, there will be a limit on the amounts of wheat and/or barley he can produce, a limit that can be increased only with an increase in the acreage of land at the farmer's disposal. In other words the supply of land *limits*, *constrains*, or *restricts* the production of wheat and barley. Thus we speak of a resource setting a *limit, constraint*, or *restriction* on production.

The physical quantities of wheat or barley that can be produced in this simple model will depend on the so-called production function which relates outputs of wheat or barley to inputs of land. Let us assume the simplest of relationships. Let us suppose that 1 acre of land can produce 1 bushel of wheat *or* $\frac{1}{2}$ bushel of barley. Thus 20 acres, for instance, will produce exactly 20 bushels of wheat; or, alternatively, 25 bushels of barley will require exactly 50 acres of land.

Our farmer with his 8 acres can either allocate all the land to wheat, allocate all to barley, or divide his land between wheat and barley in any combination he chooses. Let us write this more explicitly.

Let the amount of wheat the farmer wishes to produce be x_1 bushels, and let the amount of barley be x_2 bushels. Then, since each bushel of wheat requires 1 acre of land and each bushel of barley requires 2 acres, all combinations of wheat and barley which the farmer may grow on his 8 acres are given by equation (1.1).

$$1x_1 + 2x_2 = 8 \tag{1.1}$$

This equation shows that the farmer may produce, say, 4 bushels of wheat and 2 of barley, 8 of wheat and none of barley, 4 of barley and none of wheat, and so on. Note that equation (1.1) is measured in *acres*. Each of the two terms on the left-hand side is

(number of acres required per bushel × number of bushels)

which gives the number of acres used by each product. The combination of these two acreages must add up to 8 acres.

This production situation is illustrated in Figure 1.1, in which x_1 (bushels of wheat) is measured along the vertical axis and x_2 (bushels of barley) is measured along the horizontal axis. If all 8 acres are used in wheat production, the farmer can produce 8 bushels, indicated by point A on the wheat axis x_1. If all 8 acres are used for barley, the farmer can produce 4 bushels of barley, indicated by point B on the barley axis x_2. The straight line AB shows all combinations of wheat and barley that can be produced by the 8 acres of land. This line represents equation (1.1).

The farmer, however, may not wish to use up *all* the land in this situation. It may prove profitable, for instance, to produce 4 bushels of wheat and 1 bushel of barley, a combination represented by point X in Figure 1.1. At

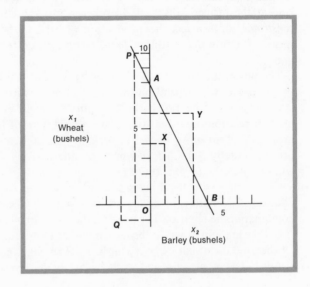

Figure 1.1

this point wheat would be using 4 acres and barley 2 acres; the remaining 2 acres of land would be idle.

Thus we are interested not merely in all combinations represented by *line AB*, but in all the possible combinations encompassed by *area OAB*. Any point outside this area, say *Y*, is regarded as being *infeasible*, because it would require a greater supply of land than the 8 acres available. Mathematically we can express any point within the feasible area *OAB* as a combination of x_1 and x_2 whose sum is *less than or equal to* 8. The *equation* (1.1) is now changed to the *inequation*

$$1x_1 + 2x_2 \leq 8 \tag{1.2}$$

Notice that the inequation (1.2) actually defines combinations of x_1 and x_2 which lie "southwest" of line *AB*, and thus some negative values of x_1 and/or x_2 would not violate this constraint. For example, at point *P* in Figure 1.1, $x_1 = 10$ and $x_2 = -1$; at point *Q*, $x_1 = -1$ and $x_2 = -2$. At *P*, the in- equation (1.2) is calculated as $1x_1 + 2x_2 = 10 - 2 = 8$, and at *Q*, $1x_1 + 2x_2 = -1 - 4 = -5$. Thus both these sets of values are consistent with the inequation (1.2), since both cause the left side of (1.2) to be less than or equal to 8. But "negative production" is clearly a concept that must be excluded from consideration. This can be done by writing

$$\begin{aligned} x_1 &\leq 0 \\ x_2 &\leq 0 \end{aligned} \tag{1.3}$$

We can now see that the combined set of inequations (1.2) and (1.3) is a complete definition of the area and boundary of the triangle *OAB*. In other words any combination of x_1 and x_2 is *feasible* if it satisfies *all* these inequations, and *infeasible* if it violates any one of them. To illustrate, point *X* in Figure 1.1 is feasible. Why? Because here $x_1 = 4$ and $x_2 = 1$. This is consistent with inequation (1.3); and $1x_1 + 2x_2 = 6$, which is less than 8 and so inequation (1.2) is satisfied too. Point *Y* is infeasible, because (1.2) is violated: here, $1x_1 + 2x_2 = 12$. Finally, *P* and *Q*, while satisfying (1.2), are both inconsistent with inequation (1.3) and are therefore infeasible.

Let us pause to define some terms. An inequality that defines the upper limit placed on production by a resource is called a *resource constraint* or *restriction*. Thus in the above example the inequation (1.2) defines the *land constraint*. The general restriction specified in inequation (1.3) is referred to as the *nonnegativity condition*. The area of feasible product combinations is called the *feasible region* (here the triangle *OAB*). Finally, the alternative production possibilities open to the entrepreneur are referred to as *activities* or *processes*. Thus in our example wheat production constitutes one activity, barley production another. The sense of these terms will emerge more clearly as we proceed.

1.2 Introduction of a Different Constraint

Again referring to our example, suppose that land is available in unlimited supply but that instead another factor, say labor, is scarce. The production of wheat and barley will now be limited solely by the availability of a fixed amount of labor, say 12 man-hours. If technological data indicate that wheat uses 3 man-hours of labor per bushel of output, while barley requires only 1 man-hour per bushel, we could either devote all 12 man-hours of labor to wheat and produce 4 bushels of x_1, or else we could devote all 12 man-hours to barley and produce 12 bushels of x_2. Alternatively we could produce some mixture of x_1 and x_2, say 1 bushel of wheat (requiring 3 man-hours) and 9 bushels of barley (requiring 9 man-hours). As before, all possible combinations of x_1 and x_2 which can be produced by the 12 man-hours of labor can be shown graphically, as indicated by the straight line CD in Figure 1.2. By exactly the same reasoning as before we can define the *line CD* mathematically as the equation

$$3x_1 + 1x_2 = 12 \qquad (1.4)$$

and the *area* within and on the edge of the triangle OCD as the inequality set

$$3x_1 + 1x_2 \leq 12 \qquad (1.5a)$$

$$x_1, x_2 \geq 0 \qquad (1.5b)$$

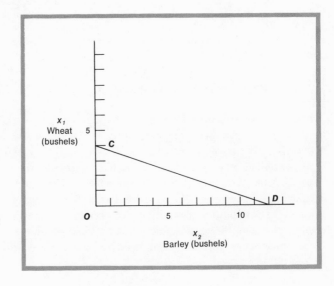

Figure 1.2

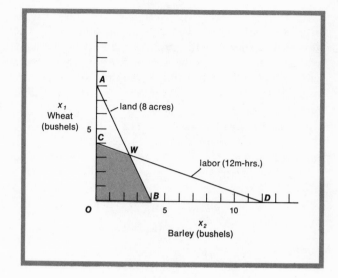

Figure 1.3

Inequation (1.5a) states that a combination of x_1 bushels of wheat and x_2 bushels of barley must be such that (3 man-hours per bushel of wheat *times* x_1 bushels produced) plus (1 man-hour per bushel of barley *times* x_2 bushels produced) must not exceed the available number of man-hours, 12. In addition (1.5b) states that neither x_1 bushels of wheat nor x_2 bushels of barley can be negative.

Thus, when labor is the only limiting resource, as in this example, the set of inequalities in (1.5) is a complete description of the feasible combinations of x_1 bushels of wheat and x_2 bushels of barley which are open to the farmer.

1.3 Superimposing Constraints

The next case to consider is that where *both* land *and* labor are in limited supply. This two-factor, two-activity model may be depicted by superimposing Figure 1.2 on Figure 1.1. The resultant diagram is Figure 1.3. Defining any point in this diagram by its coordinates (x_1, x_2), we can, as usual, immediately exclude from consideration any point (x_1, x_2) which violates our nonnegativity condition, i. e., any point which lies to the left of the vertical axis and/or below the horizontal axis. Next, remember from Figure 1.1 that any point (x_1, x_2) which lies above *AB* is infeasible with respect to land supply, and from Figure 1.2 that any point above *CD* is infeasible with respect to labor supply. Therefore, any point which lies above *either AB or CD* is infeasible when both constraints are operative. It follows that any point (x_1, x_2) in the area AWC is infeasible because, though it is feasible with respect to land, it requires more labor than is available; any point in the area WBD is infeasible because, though it is feasible with respect to labor, it requires too much land; and any point above and/or to the right of AWD is infeasible because it requires more of *both* resources than is available.

We are therefore left with the area $OCWB$ in Figure 1.3, which represents the feasible region for this two-process model, with the given resource constraints of 8 acres of land and 12 man-hours of labor. In this and subsequent diagrams showing sets of constraints the feasible region is shaded.

Mathematically this area $OCWB$ is defined by the set of inequalities

$$1x_1 + 2x_2 \le 8$$
$$3x_1 + 1x_2 \le 12 \qquad (1.6a)$$

$$x_1, x_2 \ge 0 \qquad (1.6b)$$

In other words, any combination (x_1, x_2) of wheat and barley outputs will be feasible only if it satisfies *all* the inequalities in (1.6) above.

It is apparent that we could allow for any number of limited factors in the production of these two goods, wheat and barley. Each new factor introduced, in addition to land and labor, would be represented by another straight line superimposed on Figure 1.3 and another inequation in the set in (1.6). To illustrate this, let us add one further input to the two we already have. Suppose both crops require fertilizer at the rate of one hundredweight per bushel. Then a combination of x_1 bushels of wheat and x_2 bushels of barley will require $(1x_1 + 1x_2)$ hundredweight of fertilizer. If the total amount of fertilizer available is 5 hundredweight, we can proceed as before to define a line FG representing the fertilizer constraint. The three-factor, two-product model is depicted in Figure 1.4.[1] It is obvious that our feasible region is now $OCEHB$ and that this area is defined by the set of inequalities

$$1x_1 + 2x_2 \le 8$$
$$3x_1 + 1x_2 \le 12 \qquad (1.7a)$$
$$1x_1 + 1x_2 \le 5$$

$$x_1, x_2 \ge 0 \qquad (1.7b)$$

[1] The similarity between the line $CEHB$ in Figure 1.4 and an ordinary "production possibility boundary" should be noted. In neoclassical economics the possible output combinations for two products from a given bundle of inputs is usually represented as a smooth curve concave to the origin. In Figure 1.4 the production boundary $CEHB$ is concave, but it is not smoothly curved, being composed of three linear segments, CE, EH, HB. It can be seen, however, that more and more effective constraints could be added to cause the production boundary for this two-product model to approximate more and more closely to a curve.

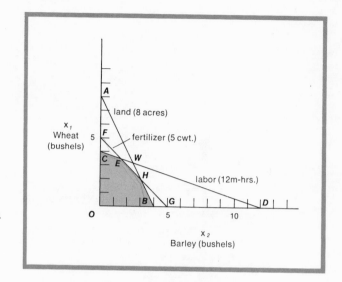

Figure 1.4

1.4   The Most Profitable Combination of Activities

Let us suppose that any amounts of wheat and barley can be sold on the market at fixed prices which, after meeting variable costs of production, transportation costs, and marketing expenses, yield the farmer a net return of $4 per bushel of wheat and $6 per bushel of barley. His total profit, z, for producing x_1 bushels of wheat and x_2 bushels of barley, is therefore

$$z = 4x_1 + 6x_2 \tag{1.8}$$

from which we can write, say,

$$x_1 = \tfrac{z}{4} - \tfrac{6}{4}x_2 \tag{1.9}$$

Equation (1.9) shows us that we could draw on Figure 1.4 a profit line which, for any level of z, would run downward from left to right with a slope of $-\tfrac{6}{4}$. Any such profit line will show all combinations of x_1 and x_2 that will yield the given total profit z.

In Figure 1.5, which contains just the production possibility boundary *CEHB* from Figure 1.4, a series of profit lines is drawn, corresponding to a series of values for z. For instance, the line P_1P_1 represents a total profit of $6. We see that this profit can be earned by producing *either* 1½ bushels of wheat, *or* 1 bushel of barley, *or* any combination (say ¾ bushel wheat and ½ bushel barley) which is consistent with the equation

$$6 = 4x_1 + 6x_2 \tag{1.10}$$

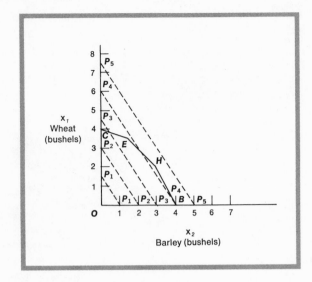

Figure 1.5

Any combination of x_1 and x_2 yielding a total profit of $12 is given by the line P_2P_2 in Figure 1.5, which represents the equation

$$12 = 4x_1 + 6x_2 \qquad (1.11)$$

In Figure 1.5 we have taken $z = 6$, 12, 18, 24, and 30, and drawn the corresponding profit lines $P_1P_1, P_2P_2, P_3P_3, P_4P_4$, and P_5P_5. The further a profit line is from the origin of the figure, the higher is the total net profit it represents.

Now, since we assume the farmer's goal is profit maximization, he will wish to produce a combination of wheat and barley touching the profit line furthest from the origin. Since resource supplies limit his feasible choices to the area $OCEHB$, it is apparent that the most profitable combination will lie at H. The total profit at this point, lying between P_4P_4 and P_5P_5, will be somewhere between $24 and $30. We can read from the graph that this profit-maximizing combination is given where $x_1 = 2$, $x_2 = 3$, i.e., a production of 2 bushels of wheat and 3 bushels of barley. From equation (1.8) we can calculate that total profit at point H is $(4 \times 2) + (6 \times 3) = \$26$.

Referring to Figure 1.4 we notice that point H lies on both the land and the fertilizer constraints, but "inside" the labor constraint. In other words, this combination of $x_1 = 2$ and $x_2 = 3$ uses up all available land and fertilizer, but not all the labor supply. This can be checked with the constraint inequations in (1.7). At our optimum combination the value of the left side of the land constraint, $(1x_1 + 2x_2)$ is equal to $(1 \times 2) + (2 \times 3)$, which equals 8 acres, the given land supply. Similarly the left side of the fertilizer constraint works out at $(1x_1 + 1x_2) = (1 \times 2) + (1 \times 3) = 5$ hundredweight, again just exhausting the supply. Finally, the value of the labor constraint is $(3x_1 + 1x_2) = (3 \times 2) + (1 \times 3) = 9$ man-hours, which is less than the 12 man-hours available. In other words, at the optimum combination of wheat and barley production, land and fertilizer inputs are fully utilized, but 3 man-hours of labor are left unused.

1.5 Formal Expression of the Wheat/Barley Problem

If profit maximization is our objective, the overall problem could be stated as that of determining a combination of x_1 and x_2 within the feasible region such that the quantity z in equation (1.8) is as large as possible.

Thus, given the above data, we can formally express our linear programming problem as:
Maximize

$$z = 4x_1 + 6x_2 \tag{1.12a}$$

subject to

$$\begin{aligned} 1x_1 + 2x_2 &\leq 8 \\ 3x_1 + 1x_2 &\leq 12 \\ 1x_1 + 1x_2 &\leq 5 \end{aligned} \tag{1.12b}$$

and

$$\begin{aligned} x_1 &\geq 0 \\ x_2 &\geq 0 \end{aligned} \tag{1.12c}$$

More generally, let the net profits (or prices) for the two producing activities in the above problem be c_1 and c_2, let the supplies of the three resources be b_1, b_2, and b_3 respectively, and let the resource-use coefficients be a_{ij} (where a_{ij} is the amount of the ith resource used per unit of the jth activity). Then our problem can be written as:
Maximize

$$z = c_1x_1 + c_2x_2 \tag{1.13a}$$

subject to

$$\begin{aligned} a_{11}x_1 + a_{12}x_2 &\leq b_1 \\ a_{21}x_1 + a_{22}x_2 &\leq b_2 \\ a_{31}x_1 + a_{32}x_2 &\leq b_3 \end{aligned} \tag{1.13b}$$

and

$$\begin{aligned} x_1 &\geq 0 \\ x_2 &\geq 0 \end{aligned} \tag{1.13c}$$

EXERCISES

1. Taking the data from this chapter, show how Figure 1.4 would change if the following alterations in factor supply occurred separately, other things remaining constant:
   a. The supply of land increased to 10 acres.
   b. The supply of labor decreased to 10 man-hours.
   c. The supply of fertilizer increased to 6 hundredweight.
2. Examine the new shape of the feasible region if all three changes in exercise 1 occurred simultaneously.
3. With the net return of $4 per bushel and $6 per bushel for wheat and barley respectively, determine graphically the optimum combination for the problems in exercises 1 and 2.
4. Draw on a graph a series of profit lines, at the total profit levels shown, for the following prices of wheat and barley.
   a. Wheat $4 per bushel; barley $3 per bushel; total profit: $6, $12, $18, $24
   b. Wheat $4 per bushel; barley $10 per bushel; total profit: $20, $40, $60
   c. Wheat $7 per bushel; barley $6 per bushel; total profit: $14, $28, $42, $56
   d. Wheat $4 per bushel; barley $0 per bushel; total profit: $5, $10, $15, $20
5. Using each set of profit lines from exercise 4, determine graphically the maximum profit combinations of wheat and barley for each part of exercises 1 and 2. Calculate both the amounts of all factors used and the exact total profit at each optimum point.
6. Taking again the original data from the example in this chapter, show how Figure 1.4 would change if the following changes occurred separately in input-output coefficients, other things remaining constant:
   a. Wheat production rose to 2 bushels per acre.
   b. Barley production fell to $\frac{4}{5}$ bushels per acre.
   c. Wheat required 1 man-hour of labor per bushel and barley required 3 man-hours per bushel.
   d. Wheat required no fertilizer.
   Write out algebraically the new constraints in each case.
7. Write out algebraically the complete set of constraints that would obtain if all the changes in exercise 6 occurred simultaneously. From this, construct graphically the feasible region. Discuss the effect on the profit maximization problem of each constraint.

2

A SIMPLE
MINIMIZATION PROBLEM

2.1 The Nature of a
Minimum Constraint

The problem analyzed in Chapter 1 was one of maximization subject to maximum constraints; i.e., the objective was to determine what levels of wheat and barley production would maximize net profit, subject to maximum constraints specifying that the total use of each factor of production should not exceed its availability. Exactly analogous reasoning can be applied to the reverse situation of minimization subject to minimum constraints. Let us consider again a simple hypothetical example.

A supplier of animal-feeding stuffs has two raw materials, cornmeal and fishmeal, which he can mix together in any proportions to produce a blended feed meeting certain requirements. Suppose he knows that both cornmeal and fishmeal contain 1 unit of protein per ton. Now imagine that he receives an order for a feed which contains *at least* 4 units of protein. We can see that he can meet this order by supplying a feed made up entirely of 4 tons of cornmeal; equivalently he can supply 4 tons of fishmeal; or else he might combine cornmeal and fishmeal in a mixture whose total protein content is at least 4 units.

If x_1 represents the amount of cornmeal used to make up the required feed and x_2 the amount of fishmeal used, then the combinations of the two raw materials that will meet a specification of *exactly* 4 units of protein can be written as

$$1x_1 + 1x_2 = 4 \qquad (2.1)$$

However, the customer's specification asks for a feed containing *at least* 4 units of protein. Thus combinations of the two raw materials that yield *more* than 4 units are allowable. The range of admissible combinations of x_1 and x_2 is therefore expressed by the inequality

$$1x_1 + 1x_2 \geq 4 \tag{2.2}$$

Again, since we cannot provide 4 units of protein by mixing, say, 5 tons of cornmeal and -1 tons of fishmeal, we must also write

$$\begin{aligned} x_1 &\geq 0 \\ x_2 &\geq 0 \end{aligned} \tag{2.3}$$

to exclude negative values.

This set of inequations (2.2) and (2.3) again separates feasible from infeasible combinations of x_1 and x_2. Thus, for instance, a combination $x_1 = 3$ and $x_2 = 4$ is feasible, since both x_1 and x_2 are positive, and the protein content of this mixture is calculated from the left-hand side of (2.2) as $(1 \times 3) + (1 \times 4) = 7$ units of protein, which is greater than the required minimum of 4 units. On the other hand, $x_1 = 2$ and $x_2 = 1$ is an infeasible combination, since $(1 \times 2) + (1 \times 1) = 3$ units of protein, which violates the inequality (2.2).

Figure 2.1 depicts the inequation set (2.2) and (2.3) by shading in the feasible combinations of the two raw materials. In Figure 2.1 the line AB represents the "protein constraint," since it shows those combinations of cornmeal and fishmeal which *exactly* satisfy the protein specification for the feed.[1] Remember that, to be *feasible* with respect to protein requirement, a combination (x_1, x_2) may lie anywhere along AB, on the x_1 axis above A or on the x_2 axis to the right of B, or in the region above or to the right of AB. In other words, a feasible combination must lie inside or on the edge of the *shaded* area of Figure 2.1.

2.2 Introduction of a Different Constraint

Now suppose that the producer receives an order for another feed, this one to contain *at least* 6 units of oil. Let us imagine that cornmeal contains 1 unit of oil per ton and fishmeal contains 3 units per ton. Then a feed containing *exactly* 6 units of oil could be made from either 6 tons of cornmeal or 2 tons of fishmeal, or from some combination of these two components. If, as before, we let $x_1 =$ amount of cornmeal used and $x_2 =$

[1] Parallel to the reasoning of Chapter 1, if all 4 units of protein were to be supplied entirely by cornmeal, we would require 4 tons of it, indicated by point A on the x_1 axis in Figure 2.1. If, instead, all 4 units were provided entirely by fishmeal, we would require 4 tons of x_2, point B in Figure 2.1. The straight line joining A and B indicates all combinations of cornmeal and fishmeal yielding exactly 4 units of protein.

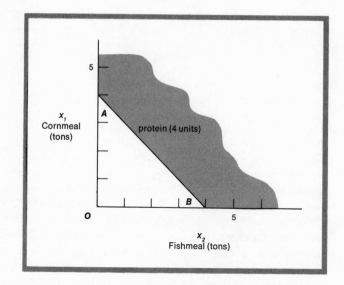

Figure 2.1

amount of fishmeal, we can write all combinations of the two raw materials which *exactly* meet the oil requirement as

$$1x_1 + 3x_2 = 6 \qquad (2.4)$$

Again, we wish to allow also for combinations that provide *more* than the minimum requirements of oil, and we wish to exclude negative quantities of cornmeal and fishmeal. So, we should write equation (2.4) as the inequality set

$$1x_1 + 3x_2 \geq 6 \qquad (2.5a)$$

$$x_1, x_2 \geq 0 \qquad (2.5b)$$

Just as the inequation set (2.3) defines the area of feasible combinations of the two raw materials with respect to the protein content of the feed mix, so inequation (2.5) delineates the feasible region for the oil content of this mix. Figure 2.2 depicts the feasible region given by (2.5); the line CD is called the "oil constraint," and again the shaded area is feasible.

2.3 Superimposing Constraints

Let us suppose now that a customer orders a feed which must contain, simultaneously, at least 4 units of protein and at least 6 units of oil. This means that combinations of x_1 and x_2 must now satisfy *both* the inequality sets (2.3) and (2.5). That is, our feasible region can now be defined by the inequality set (2.6):

$$1x_1 + 1x_2 \geq 4$$
$$1x_1 + 3x_2 \geq 6$$

(2.6a)

$$x_1, x_2 \geq 0$$

(2.6b)

A pictorial representation of this constraint set will involve superimposing Figure 2.1 on Figure 2.2. This is shown in Figure 2.3. Using the same reasoning as in the previous chapter, we can outline the new feasible region by eliminating the areas of infeasibility. First, any point to the left of the vertical axis or below the horizontal axis is excluded by the nonnegativity condition. Any point in the triangle CAE is infeasible with respect to the oil constraint alone, and any point in the triangle EDB is infeasible with respect to the protein constraint alone. Finally any point within the area $OAED$ violates *both* constraints; i.e., a combination of cornmeal and fishmeal in this area does not supply enough of either protein or oil to meet the given specifications. We are thus left with the shaded area on Figure 2.3 as the feasible region. In other words all combinations of x_1 and x_2 supplying at least 4 units of protein and 6 units of oil will lie *within* or *on the edge of* the area whose boundary is $QCEBR$ (where Q and R are an infinite distance from O).

It is now obvious that we could add further specifications to this problem in the form of additional minimum requirements for ingredients of a feed

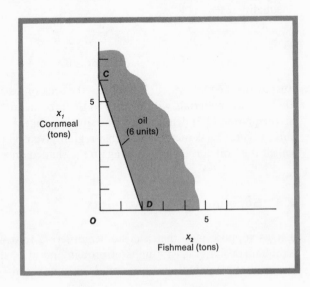

Figure 2.2

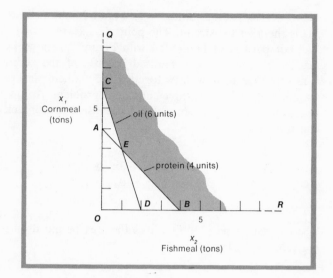

Figure 2.3

mix made from these two raw materials. *CEB*, the lower part of the boundary of the feasible region in Figure 2.3, is a "curve" made up of two linear segments. We can see that by adding further minimum constraints to our problem, we could gradually convert this boundary into a near-smooth curve, convex to the origin. Let us illustrate this procedure by adding one further restriction.

Suppose that in addition to the protein and oil specifications dealt with above, a customer requires a feed containing at least 14 units of fiber. Suppose the manufacturer knows that fishmeal contains no fiber at all, whereas cornmeal contains 7 units of fiber per ton. Then he will calculate that for the fiber content to be met, the final mixture must contain *at least* 2 tons of cornmeal. This relationship can be written as

$$7x_1 \geq 14 \tag{2.7}$$

which states that the total number of units of fiber in a given feed mix (i.e., the number of units of fiber in each ton of cornmeal *times* the number of tons of cornmeal) must be equal to or greater than the minimum requirement of 14 units. To be clearer we might write

$$7x_1 + 0x_2 \geq 14 \tag{2.8}$$

in order to make explicit the fact that fishmeal contains no fiber.

Graphically we represent the fiber constraint of inequation (2.8) as a straight line parallel with the horizontal axis in Figure 2.3 and intersecting the vertical axis at the point $x_1 = 2.$[2] Figure 2.4 shows the resultant diagram. FG is the fiber constraint. The point G, like the point R, is at infinity.

A comparison of Figure 2.4 with Figure 2.3 shows by how much the feasible region has been reduced because of the addition of the fiber constraint. Let us now draw together the mathematical description of the feasible region for this three-constraint problem. Any point (x_1, x_2) will be feasible for this problem only if it is consistent with each of the following constraints:

$$
\begin{aligned}
1x_1 + 1x_2 &\geq 4 \\
1x_1 + 3x_2 &\geq 6 \\
7x_1 + 0x_2 &\geq 14
\end{aligned}
\tag{2.9a}
$$

$$
x_1, x_2 \geq 0
\tag{2.9b}
$$

The inequation set (2.9) describes the area bounded on its lower side by $QCEHG$ in Figure 2.4.

2.4 Least-Cost Combination

Knowing the minimum specifications for the above feed mix, the producer will, we assume, wish to choose a combination of the two raw materials that will minimize his total costs. Suppose cornmeal costs $3 per ton and fishmeal costs $5 per ton. Then the total cost z of a mixture containing x_1 tons of cornmeal and x_2 tons of fishmeal will be

$$
z = 3x_1 + 5x_2
\tag{2.10}
$$

Hence we can write

$$
x_1 = \tfrac{z}{3} - \tfrac{5}{3}x_2
\tag{2.11}
$$

Thus, for any total cost z, we could draw a line on Figure 2.4 representing all combinations of x_1 and x_2 incurring this given total cost. Equation (2.11) tells us that for any z, the total cost line will have a slope of $-\tfrac{5}{3}$. In other words, total cost z will be held constant only if, for every unit of x_2 added, $\tfrac{5}{3}$ units of x_1 are withdrawn.

Figure 2.5 shows a series of cost lines, corresponding to a series of values for z. For instance, consider every combination of x_1 and x_2 whose cost totals $15. Taking equation (2.10) and setting $z = 15$, we can see that a cost of $15 is incurred by any combination of the two raw materials satisfying the equation

$$
15 = 3x_1 + 5x_2
\tag{2.12}
$$

[2] Two tons of cornmeal supply 14 units of fiber, indicated by point F on the x_1 axis in Figure 2.4. An infinite amount of fishmeal, however, cannot produce the required 14 units of fiber; hence there is no corresponding point on the horizontal axis from which a straight line may be joined to F. Thus the straight line through F is parallel to the x_2 axis.

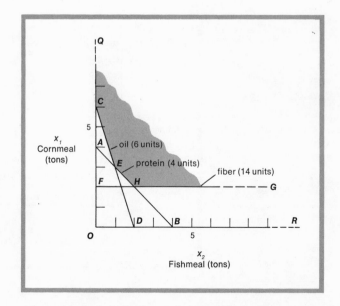

Figure 2.4

A mix containing no fishmeal would require 5 tons of cornmeal to incur a total cost of \$15; this gives point P_2 on the x_1 axis of Figure 2.5. Similarly the same cost would arise from a mix containing 3 tons of fishmeal and no cornmeal, giving point P_2 on the horizontal axis. The line P_2P_2 thus represents all combinations of x_1 and x_2 which incur a total cost of \$15. Similarly P_4P_4 is the cost line for $z = 30$, representing all combinations of the two raw materials satisfying the equation

$$30 = 3x_1 + 5x_2 \qquad (2.13)$$

For illustrative purposes, only four cost lines, P_1P_1, P_2P_2, P_3P_3, P_4P_4, out of an infinite number have been drawn on Figure 2.5, corresponding to total costs of \$7.50, \$15, \$22.50, and \$30 respectively. Observe that as z increases, the cost line moves further from the origin. Thus, since the feed-mix producer wishes to minimize costs, he will aim to be on the cost line which is lowest, i.e., closest to the origin. Given that the feasible region is bounded by $QCEHG$, it is apparent from the figure that the feasible point which is on the closest cost line to the origin is E. We read from Figure 2.5 that this point indicates a mixture of 3 tons cornmeal and 1 ton fishmeal as the least-cost combination; the total cost of this mixture will, in fact, be just less than \$15, since E lies just below the P_2P_2 cost line. From equation (2.10), setting $x_1 = 3$ and $x_2 = 1$, we calculate the total cost exactly as \$14.

Looking back to Figure 2.4 we notice that point E lies *on* both the protein and oil constraint lines but *above* the fiber constraint line. In

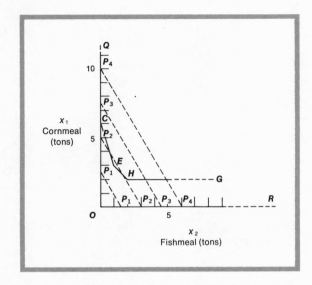

Figure 2.5

other words the combination of $x_1 = 3$ and $x_2 = 1$ *just* meets the protein and oil specifications for the feed, but overfulfills the fiber requirement. This fact can be checked against the constraint inequations in (2.9). At our optimum combination, 3 tons of cornmeal and 1 ton of fishmeal, the value of the left side of the protein constraint, $(1x_1 + 1x_2)$ becomes $(1 \times 3) + (1 \times 1) = 4$, which just satisfies the protein requirement. Similarly the left side of the oil constraint, $(1x_1 + 3x_2)$, works out at $(1 \times 3) + (3 \times 1) = 6$, again just meeting the specification. Finally the fiber constraint, $(7x_1 + 0x_2)$, is calculated as $(7 \times 3) + (0 \times 1) = 21$, which means that this mixture contains 7 units of fiber above the minimum requirement for this ingredient.

2.5 Formal Expression of This Feed-Mix Problem

If cost minimization is our objective, the overall problem could be stated as that of determining a combination of x_1 and x_2 within the feasible region such that the quantity z in equation (2.10) is as small as possible.

Thus, given the above data, we can formally express this linear programming problem as:
Minimize

$$z = 3x_1 + 5x_2 \tag{2.14a}$$

subject to

$$1x_1 + 1x_2 \geq 4$$
$$1x_1 + 3x_2 \geq 6 \qquad (2.14b)$$
$$7x_1 + 0x_2 \geq 14$$

and

$$x_1 \geq 0$$
$$x_2 \geq 0 \qquad (2.14c)$$

In more general notation, let the net costs for the two raw materials of the mixture in the above problem be c_1 and c_2, let the minimum levels of the three constraints be b_1, b_2, and b_3 respectively, and let the input-output coefficients be a_{ij}, where a_{ij} is the amount of the ith ingredient provided by each unit of the jth raw material. Then our problem can be written as:

Minimize

$$z = c_1 x_1 + c_2 x_2 \qquad (2.15a)$$

subject to

$$a_{11}x_1 + a_{12}x_2 \geq b_1$$
$$a_{21}x_1 + a_{22}x_2 \geq b_2 \qquad (2.15b)$$
$$a_{31}x_1 + a_{32}x_2 \geq b_3$$

and

$$x_1 \geq 0$$
$$x_2 \geq 0 \qquad (2.15c)$$

EXERCISES

1. Taking the data from the feed-mix example in this chapter, show how Figure 2.4 would change if the following alterations in ingredient requirements occurred separately, other things remaining equal:
   a. The protein requirement was increased to 5 units.
   b. The oil requirement was reduced to 5 units.
   c. The fiber requirement was increased to 21 units.
2. Examine the new shape of the feasible region if all three changes in exercise 1 occurred simultaneously.
3. Given net costs of $3 per ton and $5 per ton for cornmeal and fishmeal respectively, determine optimum combinations for the problems in exercises 1 and 2.
4. Draw on a graph a series of cost lines, at the total cost levels shown, for the following unit costs of cornmeal and fishmeal:
   a. Cornmeal $30 per ton and fishmeal $50 per ton; total cost: $75, $150, $225, $300

    b. Cornmeal $5 per ton and fishmeal $2 per ton; total cost: $5, $10, $15, $20

    c. Cornmeal $1 per ton and fishmeal $10 per ton; total cost: $5, $10, $15, $20

5. For the original problem as set up in this chapter and for the revised problems in exercise 1, determine graphically the minimum cost combinations of cornmeal and fishmeal, using in turn each set of cost lines from exercise 4. Calculate total costs and the amounts of each ingredient supplied at each optimum combination of raw materials.

6. Examine the effects on Figure 2.4 if the following changes occurred separately in the a_{ij} coefficients which show the amounts of each ingredient supplied by each raw material, everything else remaining constant:

    a. Fishmeal supplied 1 unit of fiber per ton.

    b. Fishmeal supplied $\frac{1}{3}$ unit of protein per ton.

    c. Cornmeal supplied no oil.

In each case, write the new constraint in its algebraic form.

7. Construct graphically the feasible region if all three changes in exercise 6 occurred simultaneously. What is the new least-cost combination and what is its cost?

3

SLACK VARIABLES

3.1 Slack Variables for Maximum Constraints

Recall the simple production problem in Chapter 1 where 8 acres of land had to be allocated between two activities, wheat and barley. In that problem it was stated that the farmer may not wish to use up *all* the land in this situation. It may prove profitable, for instance, to produce 4 bushels of wheat and 1 bushel of barley: 4 bushels of wheat would be using 4 acres, 1 bushel of barley would require 2 acres, and the remaining 2 acres of land would be idle. We therefore changed from an equation, (1.1), to an inequation, (1.2). This inequation together with the nonnegativity condition (1.3) defined a region of combinations of x_1 bushels of wheat and x_2 bushels of barley which were feasible with respect to the given 8 acres' supply of land. We now wish to show how the inequation (1.2) can be rewritten as an *equation* that will, with the nonnegativity condition, equivalently describe the feasible region. One important reason for making this conversion is that, in solving subsequent linear programming problems, it will prove much simpler to deal with sets of simultaneous equations rather than sets of simultaneous inequations. As we shall see in this chapter, the conversion has economic significance as well.

In Figure 3.1 the land constraint AB from our maximization problem in Chapter 1 is drawn. Point X indicates a combination of x_1 and x_2 at which some land is left unused. Previously we have indicated that idle land is possible at any combination (x_1, x_2) by means of an inequality sign, as in inequation (3.1):

$$1x_1 + 2x_2 \leq 8 \tag{3.1}$$

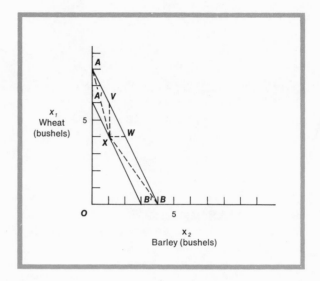

Figure 3.1

Now let us introduce a specific variable, s_1, to represent that amount of land, if any, which is left unused with any feasible combination of x_1 and x_2. Thus, instead of the inequality in (3.1), we may now write the exact statement

$$1x_1 + 2x_2 + 1s_1 = 8 \tag{3.2}$$

This equation is read as follows: (1 acre of land per bushel of wheat *times* x_1 bushels of wheat) *plus* (2 acres of land per bushel of barley *times* x_2 bushels of barley) *plus* (1 *times* the number of acres of land unused) must equal 8 acres. We can see that any combination of x_1 bushels of wheat and x_2 bushels of barley in the feasible region will now be capable of strictly satisfying equation (3.2), because the new variable, s_1, can simply adjust itself to "mop up any leftover." Thus, for example, if $x_1 = 4$ and $x_2 = 1$, then s_1 must equal 2 and (3.2) holds.

This can be confirmed graphically by looking at point X in Figure 3.1, where $x_1 = 4$ and $x_2 = 1$. The amount of slack land at this point is measured by the distance of X from the land constraint AB. Let us look first at the distance between X and, say, A. Moving from X to A involves an increase of 4 bushels in wheat output (since x_1 increases from 4 to 8 bushels) and a sacrifice of 1 bushel of barley production (since x_2 reduces from 1 bushel to zero). This movement may be expressed equivalently in terms of acres of land. An increase of 4 bushels in wheat output would require (1 acre per bushel × 4 bushels) = 4 acres of land; simultaneously a decrease of barley output by 1 bushel would release (2 acres per bushel × 1 bushel) = 2 acres of land. Thus the net "requirement" of land in

24

moving from X to A would be $4 - 2 = 2$ acres. This is the "distance," in terms of land, between X and A, and confirms the value of s_1 at this point, which we calculated from equation (3.2).

Similarly we might have measured the distance between X and AB as the distance XB. Moving from X to B involves an increase in barley output of 3 bushels, equivalent to $2 \times 3 = 6$ acres of land; it also requires a sacrifice of 4 bushels of wheat production, equivalent to $1 \times 4 = 4$ acres of land. The net requirement of land in moving from X to B is thus $6 - 4 = 2$ acres, reconfirming our above calculations.

Graphically, it is easiest to calculate the amount of slack resource at a given point by measuring either the *vertical* or the *horizontal* distance between the point and the relevant constraint. Thus in Figure 3.1 the distance XV is measured simply as 2 bushels of x_1, which, at 1 acre per bushel of wheat, is equivalent to 2 acres of land, which equals s_1. Alternatively, XW is measured as 1 bushel of barley, which, at 2 acres per bushel, is equivalent again to 2 acres of land.

An alternative way of viewing point X in Figure 3.1 is to consider it as lying on a new land constraint $A'B'$, which is parallel to the original constraint AB. Any point along $A'B'$ represents a combination of x_1 and x_2 requiring a total of only 6 acres of land. Since any point on AB represents a combination requiring 8 acres, it follows that the distance between any point on $A'B'$ and any point on AB is equivalent to 2 acres of land. As we have seen, it is this distance which is measured by the variable s_1 in equation (3.2).

The variable s_1 is called a "slack variable" for the obvious reason that it takes up any "slack" left when a feasible combination of real activities is chosen.[1] Let us illustrate further by looking again at equation (3.2). If $x_1 = 0$ and $x_2 = 2\frac{1}{2}$, we can see that s_1 must be 3 for equation (3.2) to hold. Alternatively, if $x_1 = 2$ and $x_2 = 3$, s_1 must be zero, since at this combination *all* the land is being used up by the "real" activities and none is therefore idle. At the other extreme, when $x_1 = 0$ and $x_2 = 0$, all the land is unused and s_1 must equal 8 acres.

It should now be apparent that s_1 *must*, like the real variables x_1 and x_2, remain nonnegative. If it were negative, equation (3.2) could represent a point outside the feasible region. For example, if s_1 were equal to -2, equation (3.2) would become $1x_1 + 2x_2 - 2 = 8$, or $1x_1 + 2x_2 = 10$. Thus a combination such as $x_1 = 9$ and $x_2 = \frac{1}{2}$ would become possible, which uses more land than the available supply. The condition

$$s_1 \geq 0 \tag{3.3}$$

ensures that the equation (3.2) remains exactly equivalent to the inequality (3.1).

---

[1] Slack variables are sometimes also known as *disposal* variables, because the processes they represent indicate nonuse or *disposal* of a resource.

Now let us define a slack variable for the labor constraint in our maximization problem. Let s_2 be the amount of labor left unused by any feasible combination of x_1 and x_2. We may now write the labor constraint from (1.5) as the equation

$$3x_1 + 1x_2 + 1s_2 = 12 \qquad \text{(3.4a)}$$

$$s_2 \geq 0 \qquad \text{(3.4b)}$$

Equation (3.4a) is read as follows: (3 man-hours per bushel of wheat *times* x_1 bushels) *plus* (1 man-hour per bushel of barley *times* x_2 bushels) *plus* (1 *times* the number of man-hours of labor unused) must equal 12 man-hours. Figure 3.2 illustrates this. Let interior point X denote a combination $x_1 = 2$, $x_2 = 1$. Suppose that X lies on a "new" labor constraint $C'D'$ parallel to CD, which is constructed to represent a labor availability of only 7 man-hours, calculated from the total labor requirement at X, i.e., $(3 \times 2) + (1 \times 1)$ man-hours. (The points at which this constraint meets the axes can be calculated as follows: if all 7 man-hours were devoted to wheat, $\frac{7}{3}$, or $2\frac{1}{3}$, bushels of wheat could be produced; if, instead, the 7 man-hours were all devoted to barley, 7 bushels of barley could be produced. This gives the points C' and D' in Figure 3.2.) Now, any point on $C'D'$ will require $(12 - 7) = 5$ man-hours less than any point along CD. For example, the distance $W'X$ is equal to the distance CC', since the figure $CW'XC'$ is a parallelogram. Thus the vertical length

Figure 3.2

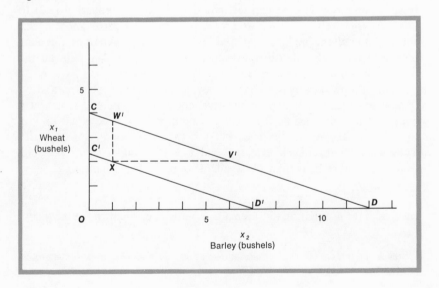

of $W'X$ measures $1\frac{2}{3}$ bushels of wheat, which require $1\frac{2}{3} \times 3 = 5$ man-hours of labor. Alternatively, the horizontal distance XV' is equal to $D'D$, which in turn measures 5 bushels of barley, also requiring 5 man-hours of labor. These graphical calculations of the value of $s_2 = 5$ for the combination $x_1 = 2$, $x_2 = 1$ confirm the value derived directly from equation (3.4a) since $(3 \times 2) + (1 \times 1) + (1 \times 5) = 12$.

Finally, if we let s_3 represent the slack variable corresponding to the fertilizer constraint, we can rewrite our constraint set from (1.7) as follows (isolating one "column" for each variable):

$$
\begin{aligned}
1x_1 + 2x_2 + 1s_1 \qquad\qquad\quad &= 8 \\
3x_1 + 1x_2 \qquad\; + 1s_2 \qquad\;\; &= 12 \\
1x_1 + 1x_2 \qquad\qquad\; + 1s_3 &= 5
\end{aligned}
\tag{3.5a}
$$

$$
\begin{aligned}
x_1, x_2 &\geq 0 \\
s_1, s_2, s_3 &\geq 0
\end{aligned}
\tag{3.5b}
$$

Formally speaking, any positive values of x_1 and x_2 will be a feasible solution to this three-constraint problem only if values of s_1, s_2, and s_3 can be found such that the equations in (3.5) are strictly satisfied. For instance, the combination $x_1 = 1$ and $x_2 = 2$ is feasible, since allowing $s_1 = 3$, $s_2 = 7$, and $s_3 = 2$ will satisfy (3.5). Similarly, the point of zero production is feasible, since with $x_1 = 0$ and $x_2 = 0$ we have $s_1 = 8$, $s_2 = 12$, and $s_3 = 5$. In this case all resources are completely unused. By referring to Figure 1.4, the reader may verify graphically the values of the slack variables for various combinations of x_1 and x_2.

3.2 Slack Variables for Minimum Constraints

Symmetrical reasoning can be applied to the minimum constraints in the example in Chapter 2. Remember that a combination of x_1 tons of corn-meal and x_2 tons of fishmeal which would exactly meet, for example, the oil specification was given by

$$
1x_1 + 3x_2 = 6
\tag{3.6}
$$

which we then discarded in favor of the inequality form

$$
1x_1 + 3x_2 \geq 6
\tag{3.7}
$$

to allow for combinations of cornmeal and fishmeal supplying *more* than the minimum specification of 6 units of oil. It is this excess supply of oil, or *overfulfillment* of the oil requirement, which is the counterpart of an *unused* input, or an *underfulfillment* of one of the resource constraints discussed in section 3.1. As we should expect, however, the coefficient of a slack variable in a minimum constraint is -1, the opposite sign to that used in a maximum constraint. In the case of an unused input, idle land for instance, the slack variable had to be *added* to the amount of land used by the real activities in order that the total land use was made equal to its availability. In the case of a minimum constraint on the oil content of a feed, on the other hand, the slack or the "surplus" variable has to be *subtracted* from the total amount of oil actually supplied by the real activities (cornmeal and fishmeal) in order to bring the total back to the minimum oil requirement.

An example should make this clear. We know that a combination of 5 tons of cornmeal and 2 tons of fishmeal is feasible because it supplies $(1 \times 5) + (3 \times 2) = 11$ units of oil, which is in excess of the minimum specification of 6 units given by inequation (3.7). In order to bring the total amount of oil actually supplied, 11 units, down to the specified minimum of 6 units, we must *subtract* from the 11 units the 5 surplus units.

If we let the surplus oil content be represented by a variable s_1 and give it a negative coefficient, we can replace the inequality (3.2) by the equation

$$1x_1 + 3x_2 - 1s_1 = 6 \tag{3.8}$$

This equation is read as follows: (1 unit of oil per ton of cornmeal *times* x_1 tons) *plus* (3 units of oil per ton of fishmeal *times* x_2 tons) *minus* (1 *times* the number of surplus units of oil) must equal 6 units of oil. The last term on the left side of (3.8) can be interpreted as (-1) *times* $(+s_1)$; in other words, we can conveniently measure s_1 as a *nonnegative* variable in this case, simply by attributing to it a negative coefficient, -1. Thus, again we must write

$$s_1 \geq 0 \tag{3.9}$$

in order to prevent the appearance of infeasible combinations of x_1 and x_2.

We can now see, to take another example, that a combination of $x_1 = 3$ and $x_2 = 6$ is feasible with respect to the oil constraint, since s_1 can adjust to 15, giving a value for the left side of (3.8) of $(1 \times 3) + (3 \times 6) + (-1 \times 15) = 6$. On the other hand, $x_1 = 2$ and $x_2 = 1$ is infeasible, since no *nonnegative* value of s_1 can bring the left side of equation (3.8) to equal 6.

As before, we can verify this graphically. Figure 3.3 shows the oil constraint CD from our minimization problem. The feasible point X, where $x_1 = 3$ and $x_2 = 2$, may be considered as lying on a new oil constraint $C'D'$ corresponding to an oil requirement of $(1 \times 3) + (3 \times 2) = 9$ units. Thus, since any point on CD corresponds to a combination supplying 6 units of oil, any point on $C'D'$, such as point X, must overfulfill the oil constraint by $9 - 6 = 3$ units. As before, we may check this value from the graph as the "distance" measured in units of oil of any point on $C'D'$ from any point on CD. For example the movement from X to C involves an *increase* in cornmeal, x_1, of 3 tons, together with a *decrease* in fishmeal,

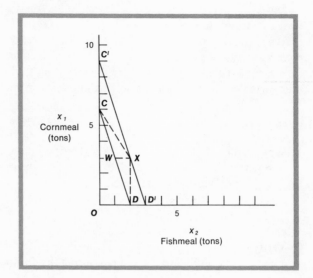

Figure 3.3

x_2, of 2 tons. Since the addition of 3 tons of cornmeal yields 3 more units of oil, while the reduction of 2 tons of fishmeal implies 6 units less of oil, there will be, on balance, a net reduction of $6 - 3 = 3$ units of oil, which corresponds to the value of s_1 calculated above. More simply, the distance between X and CD could be measured by the horizontal distance XW. This is read from Figure 3.3 as a reduction of 1 ton in x_2 which, at 3 units of oil per ton of fishmeal, is equivalent to a total reduction of 3 units of oil. These graphical measurements confirm the value calculated for s_1 from equation (3.8) for $x_1 = 3$ and $x_2 = 2$.

Defining s_2 and s_3 as the surplus variables corresponding to the minimum oil and fiber requirements respectively, we can now write the whole set of inequalities in (2.9) as follows:

$$
\begin{aligned}
1x_1 + 1x_2 - 1s_1 \qquad\qquad &= 4 \\
1x_1 + 3x_2 \qquad - 1s_2 \qquad &= 6 \\
7x_1 + 0x_2 \qquad\qquad - 1s_3 &= 14
\end{aligned}
\qquad (3.10a)
$$

$$
\begin{aligned}
x_1, x_2 &\geq 0 \\
s_1, s_2, s_3 &\geq 0
\end{aligned}
\qquad (3.10b)
$$

As in the maximization problem, any solution for the variables x_1, x_2, s_1, s_2, s_3 that satisfies both parts of (3.10) is feasible. Thus, for instance, $x_1 = 3$, $x_2 = 1$ is feasible, because values for the surplus variables of $s_1 = 0$, $s_2 = 0$, $s_3 = 7$ will allow the equations in (3.10) to be satisfied. On the other hand, $x_1 = 1$ and $x_2 = 5$ is infeasible, since with these values for

29

x_1 and x_2 there is no possible *nonnegative* value for s_3 which can satisfy the fiber constraint, the last equation in (3.10a).

Again, then, we have provided a means of representing the feasible region as a set of equations instead of a set of inequations, as previously. In subsequent chapters we shall see the importance of these slack and surplus variables in setting up and solving linear programming problems.

EXERCISES

1. What values of the slack variables s_1 (land), s_2 (labor), and s_3 (fertilizer) in equation (3.5) are implied by the following combinations of the "real" variables x_1 (wheat) and x_2 (barley)?
   a. $x_1 = 2\frac{1}{2}$ bushels, $x_2 = 1$ bushel
   b. $x_1 = 0$ bushels, $x_2 = 3$ bushels
   c. $x_1 = 2\frac{1}{2}$ bushels, $x_2 = 2\frac{1}{2}$ bushels

2. Verify the value of each slack variable in exercise 1 by pinpointing each combination on Figure 1.4 and measuring the distance of each one from each constraint.

3. Construct a table showing the values of the two real variables x_1 and x_2 and the three slack variables s_1, s_2, and s_3 at the five vertexes O, C, E, H, and B of the feasible region in Figure 1.4. What common feature do you notice about the set of values at each vertex?

4. What values of the surplus variables s_1 (protein), s_2 (oil), and s_3 (fiber) in equation (3.10) are implied by the following combinations of the real variables x_1 (cornmeal) and x_2 (fishmeal)?
   a. $x_1 = 6\frac{1}{2}$ tons, $x_2 = 0$ tons
   b. $x_1 = 4$ tons, $x_2 = 4$ tons
   c. $x_1 = 2$ tons, $x_2 = 4$ tons

5. Verify by measurement on Figure 2.4 the values of the surplus variables found in exercise 4.

6. What combinations of real and surplus variables are specified at the vertexes C, E, and H in Figure 2.4?

7. Explain, in terms of the implied values of slack and surplus variables respectively, why the points W in Figure 1.4 and F in Figure 2.4 are infeasible.

4

BASIC AND
NONBASIC VARIABLES

4.1 The Constraint System as
a Set of Simultaneous Equations

The linear programming problems we have studied so far have all involved *two* activities. We have been able to solve them by graphical means, since, as we have seen, a *two*-dimensional diagram provides a straightforward means of representing these systems. Clearly, however, a two-activity situation is just one case of a more general class of problem in which there are many activities. It should be apparent anyway that the sorts of linear programming problems encountered in real life are likely to contain more than just two activities. For example, the following is a problem containing four "real" activities which we cannot solve by graphical means:

Maximize

$$z = 125x_1 + 200x_2 + 0x_3 - 50x_4 \qquad (4.1a)$$

subject to

$$
\begin{aligned}
5x_1 + 6x_2 + 1x_3 + 0x_4 + 1s_1 &= 220 \\
8x_1 + 4x_2 - 1x_3 + 0x_4 \quad + 1s_2 &= 120 \\
1x_1 + 1x_2 + 0x_3 - 1x_4 \quad\quad + 1s_3 &= 25 \\
-16x_1 - 8x_2 + 1x_3 + 0x_4 \quad\quad\quad + 1s_4 &= 0 \\
20x_1 + 0x_2 + 0x_3 + 0x_4 \quad\quad\quad\quad - 1s_5 &= 110
\end{aligned}
\qquad (4.1b)
$$

and

$$x_1, \cdots, x_4, s_1, \cdots, s_5 \geq 0 \qquad (4.1c)$$

In the absence of many-dimensional diagrams we need a general algebraic method for solving these larger systems. One such method is the "simplex" technique. In this and subsequent chapters we shall be outlining the ideas underlying this solution procedure without actually detailing its mechanical aspects. Sufficient ground will be covered to enable the reader to set up simple linear programming problems and to interpret the sorts of solutions which might be generated for him by a computer. In Part III, the mechanical rules of the simplex technique will be presented and discussed (including, in Chapter 15, a detailed solution to the above problem). For the time being we shall use as a working example the maximization problem from Chapter 1.

Let us disregard for the time being the fact that we are trying to maximize profit, and concentrate attention on the constraint set, which for this problem is written as the set of simultaneous equations corresponding to land, labor, and fertilizer constraints respectively.

$$
\begin{aligned}
1x_1 + 2x_2 + 1s_1 \quad\quad &= 8 \\
3x_1 + 1x_2 \quad + 1s_2 \quad &= 12 \\
1x_1 + 1x_2 \quad\quad + 1s_3 &= 5
\end{aligned}
\tag{4.2}
$$

At present we are concerned only with nonnegative solutions to the set in equation (4.2). Now recall from elementary algebra that if in a set of simultaneous equations there are more unknowns than equations, there are likely to be *many* possible values for the unknowns satisfying the equations. To take the simplest example, the following system contains two unknowns and one equation:

$$
a + b = 5
\tag{4.3}
$$

It is obvious that there are many sets of possible values of a and b that will satisfy this system.

On the other hand, if a system of linear equations contains exactly as many independent equations as unknowns, there is likely to be just one set of values for the unknowns which will satisfy the equations.

Looking back to the simultaneous equations in (4.2), we see that there are five unknowns, x_1, x_2, s_1, s_2, s_3, but only three equations. Indeed the reader can easily verify that in any constraint system containing at least one real activity and also a slack or a surplus variable for each constraint, there will always be more unknowns than equations. Hence in such a system the set of constraint equations will generally have many solutions, a fact which corresponds to what we have shown to be the case in previous chapters, viz., that many feasible combinations of the five variables in this problem exist.

The approach of the simplex method, in brief, is to generate a series of solutions to the set of simultaneous equations so that one solution may eventually be chosen which maximizes the profit equation.

4.2 Tableau Representation of Simultaneous Equation Systems

It is convenient to introduce now a means of representing simultaneous equation systems such that the symbols corresponding to the unknown variables (i.e., the symbol x_1, the symbol s_2, and so on) need not be written laboriously each time the equations are set out. If we allow each variable a separate column and each equation a separate row, we can detach the coefficients from the variables and write them in the form of a tableau. We must be careful to indicate at the top of each column the variable to which the column corresponds. The right-hand sides of the equations can be grouped in a separate column, labeled "b," according to our standard terminology (see Chapter 1). There is no need to write the equals sign ($=$) in each equation. A variable not appearing in a particular row (equation) will, of course, have a zero coefficient in that row.

Thus the set of simultaneous equations in (4.2) can be written as the tableau in Table 4.1. We shall return later (section 5.3) to the incorporation of the profit equation into such a tableau.

TABLE 4.1

Real Activities		Slack Activities				Constraints
Wheat	Barley	Land	Labor	Ferti-lizer		
x_1	x_2	s_1	s_2	s_3	b	
1	2	1	0	0	8	Land
3	1	0	1	0	12	Labor
1	1	0	0	1	5	Fertilizer

4.3 A Special Solution to the Simultaneous Equations Set

In any set of m simultaneous linear equations with r unknowns, where r is greater than m, the process of deciding on values for any group of $r - m$ variables will enable an exact solution to be determined for the remaining m variables, since the system will have been reduced to m equations with m unknowns. Thus to take the simplest example, in equation (4.3), letting a equal, say, 3 immediately determines b's value as 2, since deciding on a value for a reduces the system to one having one equation and one unknown. Similarly, in the three-equation system with five variables, (4.2), the process of deciding on numerical values for any two of the five variables, say x_2 and s_3, reduces the number of unknowns in the set to three. And with three equations and three unknown variables, exact values for these three unknowns can be determined. Let us look at a special case of this.

If in any single equation a particular variable has a coefficient of unity and if every other variable either has a coefficient of zero or is itself set equal to zero, then the value of that particular variable with the unit coefficient is given as the right side of the equation. For instance take the equation

$$3a + 1c + 0d - 4e + 0f = 8 \tag{4.4}$$

In this equation the variable c has a unit coefficient; d and f have zero coefficients. If we were now to set variables a and $e = 0$, we would be left with $c = 8$. To appreciate the significance of this, refer to equation (4.2). If we were to set the values of both variables x_1 and $x_2 = 0$, we would be left with the set of equations $s_1 = 5$, $s_2 = 12$, and $s_3 = 8$. In other words the assumption that $x_1 = 0$ and $x_2 = 0$ allows us to read *directly from the right side of equation (4.2)* (*i.e., from the* b *column of Table 4.1*) a set of values for s_1, s_2, and s_3. The reason is simply that each of these variables has a unit coefficient in just one equation in which all the other variables either are zero themselves and/or have a zero coefficient.

4.4 The Identity Matrix

The above assumptions enable us to read a value from the b column for as many variables as there are equations in the set. Thus with three equations in Table 4.1, we can read off the values of the three s variables. If we isolate the submatrix corresponding to these s variables whose values are to appear in the b column, i.e., if we select from Table 4.1 each of the columns corresponding to these three s variables, we get the square matrix shown in Table 4.2. We can see that the coefficient unity appears only once in each column of this submatrix and also only once in each row. This arrangement is necessary if our above assumptions are to lead to a unique solution.[1]

A matrix consisting entirely of zeros except for a diagonal row of ones (as in Table 4.2) is called an *identity matrix*. For the properties of an identity matrix to be realized in our problem, it is not necessary for the rows and the columns to be geometrically arranged such that the unity coefficients lie neatly down the diagonal. All we need is that, by extracting

[1] Suppose the coefficient unity appeared more (or less) than just once in each row and each column of the submatrix in Table 4.2. The reader should verify that in such cases the above assumptions cannot be applied for reading off a determinate solution.

TABLE 4.2

s_1	s_2	s_3
1	0	0
0	1	0
0	0	1

the relevant columns, a square matrix be obtained, with the unity coefficients appearing exactly once in each row and once in each column.

Now, we know that when a problem of maximization subject to maximum constraints is set up, there will always be exactly as many slack variables as there are constraints. Since each slack variable has a coefficient 1 appearing in just one row and one column, it follows that we will always have an identity matrix present at the outset. Then, setting the value of each of the " real " activities (i.e., x_1 and x_2 in our example) equal to zero, the values of the slack variables will be given in the b column. Thus, for instance, Table 4.1 represents the initial solution $x_1 = 0$, $x_2 = 0$, $s_1 = 8$, $s_2 = 12$, $s_3 = 5$ for our problem. It should be evident that at this combination of values, all resources are completely slack (unused) and no " real " production is being undertaken. Graphically, looking at the diagram of this constraint set shown in Figure 4.1, we can see that this initial solution corresponds to the origin, point O.

When a linear programming problem appears with an identity matrix allowing a solution to be read off from the b column under the conditions specified above, the resultant solution is called a *basis*. The variables whose

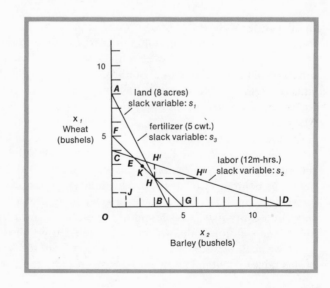

Figure 4.1

values are directly readable from the b column are called the *basic variables*, and the remaining variables, whose values are set to zero, are called *nonbasic variables*. In these simple maximization problems, if there are n " real " activities and m maximum constraints, we can see that there must be n nonbasic variables and m basic variables.

In order to form a basis we may choose as the m basic variables *any* combination of m variables from the total number of variables, both real and slack. In our numerical example, for instance, there are three rows and, therefore, *any three* variables out of the total of five (x_1, x_2, s_1, s_2, s_3) can form a basis, provided that the columns of the three variables chosen together form an identity matrix. If so, the remaining (nonbasic) variables may be set to zero, and the values for the basic variables may be read off from the b column.

We may use our example to illustrate this point. Suppose, for instance, we choose to form a basis from x_2, s_1, and s_3. Then the set of equations corresponding to this basis might appear as in equation (4.5). We use question marks (?) to denote numerical coefficients whose values we do not know yet.

$$
\begin{aligned}
?x_1 + 1x_2 \quad\quad\ + \ ?s_2 \quad\quad\ &= \ ? \\
?x_1 \quad\quad\ + 1s_1 + \ ?s_2 \quad\quad\ &= \ ? \\
?x_1 \quad\quad\quad\quad\quad\ + \ ?s_2 + 1s_3 &= \ ?
\end{aligned}
\tag{4.5}
$$

Similarly a basis formed from x_1, s_2, and s_3 might appear as in equation (4.6).

$$
\begin{aligned}
?x_2 + \ ?s_1 + 1s_2 \quad\quad\ &= \ ? \\
?x_2 + \ ?s_1 \quad\quad\ + 1s_3 &= \ ? \\
1x_1 + \ ?x_2 + \ ?s_1 \quad\quad\ &= \ ?
\end{aligned}
\tag{4.6}
$$

In tableau form these two bases appear as shown in Table 4.3. We can see from these matrixes that the columns corresponding to the basic variables form an identity matrix: these are the columns for x_2, s_1, and s_3 in the tableau from equation set (4.5), and for x_1, s_2, and s_3 in the tableau from equation set (4.6). Note that just as individual equations in a set may be written in any order, so also may the corresponding rows of a tableau be written in any order.

In any tableau the values we read off for the basic variables constitute a *basic solution*. So far, we have seen only one basic solution illustrated in full numerical detail. This was the matrix shown in Table 4.1 corresponding to the point of zero " real " production. This basis arose because of the convenient fact that when a linear programming problem is set up in this way, an identity matrix is present at the outset, formed by the slack variables. The solution contained in such a tableau is called an *initial basis*. Later we shall see how it is possible to start from the known coefficients of this tableau containing the initial basis in order to form other bases. In

TABLE 4.3

Tableau Corresponding to Equation Set (4.5)

x_1	x_2	s_1	s_2	s_3	b	Basic Variables
?	1	0	?	0	?	x_2
?	0	1	?	0	?	s_1
?	0	0	?	1	?	s_3

Tableau Corresponding to Equation Set (4.6)

x_1	x_2	s_1	s_2	s_3	b	Basic Variables
0	?	?	1	0	?	s_2
0	?	?	0	1	?	s_3
1	?	?	0	0	?	x_1

this way we shall be able to determine actual numbers to replace the unknown coefficients shown by question marks in equations (4.5), (4.6), and Table 4.3.

4.5 The Number of Variables in a Basis

We have seen that because the matrix for our maximization problem has *three* rows, to form a basis we must choose *three* basic variables. Since there are five unknowns altogether, we will have $5 - 3 = 2$ nonbasic variables, which implies that we can form a basis for feasible combinations of our five variables only by having at least two variables equal to zero. In general, we can say if a tableau has m rows and therefore m elements in the b column, there cannot be more than m variables in the solution at a nonzero level, i.e., not more than m basic variables. This means that if the number of *nonbasic* variables is n (giving a total of $[m + n]$ variables altogether) there must be at least n zero variables in the solution. In other words, at any feasible combination of variables in a given problem *we will be able to obtain a basis only if at that combination there are at least* n *variables at zero level*, to make up the set of nonbasic variables.

In Figure 4.1 let us examine for this problem the values of variables at several points in the feasible region in order to see at which points there will be at least two zero variables. From this diagram of the constraint set we may distinguish three different types of feasible combinations of real

TABLE 4.4

Point	Type	Value of Variables at This Point				
		x_1	x_2	s_1	s_2	s_3
O	Origin (vertex)	0	0	8	12	5
J	Interior	1	1	5	8	3
K	Boundary	3	2	1	1	0
H	Vertex	2	3	0	3	0

and slack variables. First there is a point, such as J, which is entirely within the feasible region. Second, there is a point, such as K, which lies on the boundary of the feasible region. Finally, there is a special class of boundary point, viz., one which lies at a corner or vertex formed by the intersection of two (or more) constraints, such as H.

Building on the discussion from Chapter 3, we can determine the values of all the variables at each of these points, as shown in Table 4.4. In this table we also include the origin, which, like H, is a vertex. As an exercise the reader may check for himself all the values of the slack variables in this table.[2]

Now observe that at the interior point J none of the five variables, x_1, x_2, s_1, s_2, s_3, has a zero value. At the nonvertex boundary point K, one variable is zero and four variables have nonzero values, while at the vertex H (and also at the origin O) there are two zero and three nonzero variables. By checking other points in the feasible region, the reader may confirm ad hoc that *only at the vertexes are there sufficient zero variables (i.e., two in this example) to enable a basis to be formed*. This fact, as we shall see, is quite satisfactory for our purposes, since the only combinations we usually wish to consider in maximization (or minimization) problems are those represented by the vertexes.

EXERCISES

The following is a set of four maximum constraints that have been converted to equalities by the addition of slack variables:

$$2x_1 + 1x_2 + 1s_1 \qquad\qquad\qquad = 8$$
$$1x_1 \qquad\quad + 1s_2 \qquad\qquad = 3$$
$$1x_1 + 1x_2 \qquad\quad + 1s_3 \qquad = 6$$
$$1x_1 \qquad\qquad\qquad\quad + 1s_4 = 5$$

with $x_1, x_2, s_1, \cdots, s_4 \geq 0$

---

[2] For example, at H all land is used (constraint AB) and all fertilizer is used (constraint FG), indicating $s_1 = 0$ and $s_3 = 0$. Labor (constraint CD) is not fully used: it is slack to the extent HH' or one bushel of wheat requiring 3 man-hours. Alternatively, slack labor s_2 can be calculated as HH'', or 3 bushels of barley. Three bushels of barley at 1 man-hour per bushel again gives a total of 3 man-hours slack.

1. How many variables will be required to form a basis for this constraint set, and how many nonbasic variables will there be?
2. What are the values of all variables at the initial basis for this problem?
3. Show how a basis may be formed from the following sets of variables:
   a. x_1, x_2, s_3, s_4
   b. x_1, s_1, s_2, s_4
   c. x_2, s_1, s_3, s_4
   Using question marks for unknown coefficients, write out the full set of equations and the full tableaux corresponding to each of these bases.
4. Using the above equations calculate the values of the slack variables s_1 to s_4 for each of the following sets of values for the real variables:
   a. $x_1 = 0,$ $x_2 = 3$
   b. $x_1 = 2,$ $x_2 = 4$
   c. $x_1 = 1,$ $x_2 = 5$
   d. $x_1 = 2,$ $x_2 = 3$
   e. $x_1 = 0,$ $x_2 = 0$
   f. $x_1 = 2\frac{1}{2}, x_2 = 3$
   At which of the above combinations are there sufficient zero variables (out of all real and slack variables) to form a basis?
5. Draw a diagram of the above set of constraints. Locate the points (a) to (f) on it from exercise 4. Classify each point (a) to (f) according to whether it lies on a vertex, on a boundary, or in the interior of the constraint set. Verify that any point at which a basis can be formed (as found in exercise 4) is a vertex of the constraint set.

5

OUTLINE OF
A SOLUTION PROCEDURE

5.1 The Idea of
Basis Transformation

Let us begin by summarizing the four major points which emerged from Chapter 4. In that chapter we learned the following, for problems of maximization subject to maximum constraints:

a. That nonnegative solutions to the set of simultaneous constraint equations represent feasible combinations of variables.
b. That there is one special class of solution to this set of equations, called a basis, enabling us to categorize basic and nonbasic variables: when the latter are set to zero, the values of the basic variables may be read from the right-hand sides of the equations.
c. That a basis can be formed from any subset of variables containing as many variables as there are constraint equations: a condition for the existence of a basis is the presence of an identity matrix corresponding to this subset of basic variables.
d. That basic solutions can represent only the *vertexes* of the feasible region described by the set of constraints.

We also wrote down sets of simultaneous equations (and corresponding tableaux) representing certain combinations of variables for our numerical problem; in these examples question marks represented unknown numerical coefficients.

In order to calculate the unknown coefficients of a tableau containing any particular subset of basic variables (say x_2, s_1, and s_3 in our example) a tableau may first be taken for which the coefficients are already *known* (in our example this would be that containing the initial basis in which the basic variables are s_1, s_2, and s_3). By applying a set of mechanical rules to this known tableau, the coefficients in the tableau for any required new basis may be generated. We still do not need to formalize the rules themselves, but it is important to understand the *manner* of their operation. This chapter, then, outlines in general terms the nature of the computational technique with which we are concerned, viz., the simplex method for linear programming.

5.2 Substituting Variables

The simplex method provides a set of rules for generating from any given basis a new one *differing from the old in respect of just one variable*. In effect, then, by use of this calculation procedure, one basic variable in the "old" solution can be made nonbasic in the "new" solution, and one nonbasic variable in the "old" solution becomes basic in the "new" solution. The procedure of a single transformation can therefore be viewed as a swap, i.e., the substitution in a given basis of any one existing nonbasic variable for any one existing basic variable. Thus, by a *series* of such transformations a basis containing any given subset of variables may be generated from a basis containing any other given subset of variables. Each step, or transformation, is called an *iteration*.

Thus it is possible *in one iteration* (i.e., with one transformation of the set of simultaneous constraint equations) to move between vertexes of the feasible region *which differ by just one variable in the basis*. For instance, in our problem it would be possible to move in one step from a point where say x_1, x_2, and s_3 are in the basis to one where say x_1, s_1, and s_3 are in the basis, since in this single iteration s_1 would replace x_2. On the other hand it would *not* be possible to move in one step from a point where x_1, x_2, and s_3 are in the basis to one where say x_2, s_1, and s_2 are in the basis, since in this movement more than one variable would need to be replaced; i.e., a *series* of iterations would be necessary.

This means, in terms of Figure 5.1 (which again represents the constraint set for our example), that in one iteration we could move from O to C or from B to H, but we would need two iterations to move from O to E (via C), or from B to E (via H). It is thus possible in one step to move from any vertex only to an adjacent vertex while staying within the feasible region. In terms of Figure 5.1 this means that we can move in a single step from one given feasible vertex to another only if the movement between them is along an edge of the region, i.e., in a straight line along an existing constraint (interpreting the two axes as constraints also, because of the nonnegativity condition).

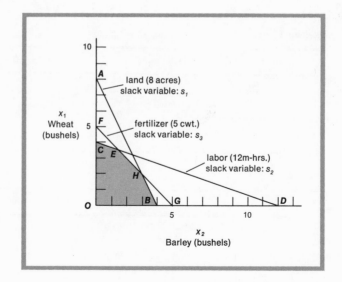

Figure 5.1

These characteristics of adjacent and nonadjacent vertexes can be verified by listing which variables are basic and which are nonbasic at each vertex, as in Table 5.1. From this table we see that adjacent vertexes differ by only one variable in the basis and that nonadjacent vertexes differ by more than one variable. The reader should verify from Figure 5.1 that at each vertex point the basic variables listed in Table 5.1 are in fact "in the

TABLE 5.1

Vertex Point	Basic Variables			Nonbasic Variables	
O	s_1	s_2	s_3	x_1	x_2
B	x_2	s_2	s_3	x_1	s_1
H	x_2	s_2	x_1	s_3	s_1
E	x_2	s_1	x_1	s_3	s_2
C	s_3	s_1	x_1	x_2	s_2

solution" at a nonzero level, and that the nonbasic variables are zero. For example, take point C. Here x_1 is obviously nonzero (in fact equal to 4 bushels of wheat), and since there exist at this point slack land and slack fertilizer, s_1 and s_3 are also nonzero. These are the three basic variables at point C. The nonbasic variables here are x_2 equal to zero, and s_2, which is zero because the point C lies on the labor constraint line CD, indicating that all labor is being used, i.e., that there is no slack labor.

Let us illustrate the beginning and the end result of a single numerical transformation by writing out the tableaux corresponding to two adjacent

TABLE 5.2

Tableau 1

x_1	x_2	s_1	s_2	s_3	b	
						Basic Variables
1	2	1	0	0	8	s_1
3	1	0	1	0	12	s_2
1	1	0	0	1	5	s_3

Tableau 2

x_1	x_2	s_1	s_2	s_3	b	
						Basic Variables
$\frac{1}{2}$	1	$\frac{1}{2}$	0	0	4	x_2
$2\frac{1}{2}$	0	$-\frac{1}{2}$	1	0	8	s_2
$\frac{1}{2}$	0	$-\frac{1}{2}$	0	1	1	s_3

vertexes for our maximization problem. Tableau 1 of Table 5.2 gives the initial basis corresponding to O in Figure 5.1 where, as we have seen, $x_1 = 0$, $x_2 = 0$, $s_1 = 8$, $s_2 = 12$, and $s_3 = 5$. Tableau 2 shows the basis corresponding to point B in Figure 5.1. From this matrix we see that the columns corresponding to the variables x_2, s_2, and s_3 form an identity matrix; thus these are the variables "in the basis" at levels read from the b column. The variables x_1 and s_1 are nonbasic and are therefore set equal to zero. The solution represented by Tableau 2 of Table 5.2 is thus $x_1 = 0$, $x_2 = 4$, $s_1 = 0$, $s_2 = 8$, $s_3 = 1$, obviously corresponding to point B in Figure 5.1. The movement from Tableau 1 to Tableau 2 in Table 5.2, i.e., from point O to point B in Figure 5.1, is achieved by one iteration of the simplex procedure. As mentioned earlier, the mechanics of the calculation of the unknown coefficients is left aside for the moment.

5.3 The Profit Equation
in the Tableau

So far, we have concentrated on the constraint set for our maximization problem, and have neglected the profit equation we are trying to maximize. Remember that in our numerical example wheat yields a net profit of $4 per bushel and barley a net profit of $6 per bushel. If we assume that the slack activities s_1, s_2, and s_3 have no monetary profit or loss attached to them, the full profit equation to be maximized may be written as follows:

$$z = 4x_1 + 6x_2 + 0s_1 + 0s_2 + 0s_3 \tag{5.1}$$

The coefficients of this equation, just like those of the constraint set, may be represented in tableau form by detaching them and writing them as a separate row above the main body of the constraint set tableau. The z coefficient from equation (5.1) can then be conveniently written as a right-hand side instead of a left-hand side, and will therefore appear under the b-column heading of the matrix. Since we have already met the notation c for these net profit figures (Chapter 1), it is appropriate to call this new row the c row. Table 5.3 shows the initial matrix for our maximization example set up with the c row in position at the top of the tableau. The other new rows in this matrix are explained below.

Since we are concerned with the maximization of profit, it is important to know, for any given basis, how profitable it would be to change this basis for a new one. In other words we wish to know, for each *nonbasic* variable, by how much total profit would change if that variable were introduced into the basis by means of the transformation procedure mentioned above. Now, this is not simply a question of how much profit (or loss) would accrue directly to each unit of the nonbasic activity introduced into the solution; it is also a question of how much loss (or profit) would arise from the consequent changes in the levels of each of the other variables *already in the basis*. To illustrate, consider a movement of the basis from point B in Figure 5.1 (basic variables x_2, s_2, s_3) to point H (basic variables x_1, x_2, s_2). It is apparent that this iteration would involve taking the basis at point B, and then, to reach H, substituting x_1 for s_3. In assessing the change in total profit resulting from this move, we would have to allow not only for the fact that each bushel of wheat (x_1) introduced into the solution would yield a profit of \$4, but also for the fact that each bushel of barley (x_2) sacrificed would result in a loss of \$6.

Thus, while the *net profits* in the c row will be the same for each basis (e.g., 1 bushel of wheat *per se* is always worth \$4), we need another row to keep account of the *net costs* associated with the introduction into the basis of each (nonbasic) activity. The coefficients in this net costs row will, of course, vary from one basis to another for any particular activity, since at different bases different variables will change at different rates as a

TABLE 5.3

x_1	x_2	s_1	s_2	s_3	b	
4	6	0	0	0	0	c row
0	0	0	0	0	0	z row
-4	-6	0	0	0	0	$z - c$ row
						Basic Variables
1	2	1	0	0	8	s_1 Slack land
3	1	0	1	0	12	s_2 Slack labor
1	1	0	0	1	5	s_3 Slack fertilizer

result of the introduction of that activity. We shall designate this new cost row the z row and enter it in the tableau immediately beneath the c row. Each coefficient of this z row measures the profits to be forgone by the introduction of a unit of each nonbasic variable. Thus the z coefficients are, in fact, *opportunity costs*.

To calculate these opportunity cost coefficients for insertion in the z row of a given tableau, we need to know for each nonbasic variable or activity:

a. The change in the level of each presently basic variable which would result from the introduction of a unit of that nonbasic variable.
b. The net profit figure (c) associated with each activity already in the basis.

It is not difficult to illustrate these calculations with the initial matrix for our example, which is shown in Table 5.3. Consider x_1, for instance. Introduction of this variable into the basis would cause changes in the values of each current basic variable s_1, s_2, and s_3. But sacrifice of slack land, slack labor, and slack fertilizer is, according to our assumptions, costless. Since no profit is forgone, the net opportunity cost of introducing x_1 into the basis will be zero.

Although we can see by inspection that the z coefficients must be zero for both nonbasic variables (x_1 and x_2) in Table 5.3, it is useful nevertheless to show in full the calculation of these z values, as it will assist our understanding when we look at another matrix. Therefore, take x_1 again as the illustration. We know, from the a coefficients in the body of the tableau, the amounts by which each slack variable will change as a result of introducing 1 unit of x_1 into the basis. Thus, reading down the column we see that 1 bushel of wheat will use up 1 acre of land, 3 man-hours of labor, and 1 hundredweight of fertilizer. Further, we know from the c row coefficients for the basic variables s_1, s_2, and s_3 the profit forgone per acre of land, per man-hour of labor, and per hundredweight of fertilizer used up. Each of these c-row coefficients is zero. Thus the total opportunity cost *per bushel of wheat introduced* is:

1 acre of land per bushel *times* $0 per acre	$0 per bushel
3 man-hrs. of labor per bushel *times* $0 per man-hour	$0 per bushel
1 cwt. of fertilizer per bushel *times* $0 per hundredweight	$0 per bushel
Total	$0 per bushel

The a coefficients in the column of each *nonbasic* activity in the body of a tableau indicate the amount of each *basic* activity which would be "displaced" if a unit of that nonbasic activity were introduced. (Thus, for example, in Table 5.3 a bushel of barley, x_2, would "displace" 2 acres of slack land, s_1, 1 man-hour of slack labor, s_2, and 1 hundredweight of slack fertilizer, s_3, if it were introduced into the basis.) These a coefficients are for this reason sometimes termed "displacement coefficients."

Let us illustrate the calculation of another set of z-row coefficients, viz., that corresponding to Tableau 2 in Table 5.2. This basis, which contains x_2, s_2, and s_3, is set up again in Table 5.4 with the c row inserted at the top of the tableau. Look first at the nonbasic variable x_1. As before, the a coefficients in the column of this activity show the amounts of each basic variable which would be displaced by the introduction of a unit of the activity. Thus, reading down the column, we see that introducing 1 bushel of wheat (x_1) would sacrifice $\frac{1}{2}$ bushel of barley (x_2), $2\frac{1}{2}$ man-hours of slack labor (s_2), and $\frac{1}{2}$ hundredweight of slack fertilizer (s_3). Inspection of the c row shows that of the three current basic variables (x_2, s_2, and s_3) whose levels will change as a result of introducing x_1, the only one with a nonzero profit coefficient is x_2; a unit of x_2 yields a profit of $6, while both s_2 and s_3 have zero coefficients in the c row. Thus the opportunity cost, the z-row coefficient, for x_1 in this tableau is:

$\frac{1}{2}$ bu. of barley displaced per bushel of wheat *times* $6 per bushel	$3 per bushel of wheat
$2\frac{1}{2}$ man-hrs. of labor displaced per bushel of wheat *times* $0 per man-hour	$0 per bushel of wheat
$\frac{1}{2}$ cwt. of fertilizer displaced per bushel of wheat *times* $0 per hundredweight	$0 per bushel of wheat
Total	$3 per bushel of wheat

In other words when the basis is at point B in Figure 5.1, the introduction of x_1 (causing the solution to move upward along the constraint AB toward the next adjacent vertex, H) will *cost* $3 per bushel of wheat introduced, because of the changes in levels of existing basic variables.

Similarly the calculation of the z-row coefficient for the other nonbasic variable in Table 5.4, viz., s_1, may be illustrated. The table shows that each unit of s_1, i.e., each acre of slack land, introduced into the basis would

TABLE 5.4

x_1	x_2	s_1	s_2	s_3	b	
4	6	0	0	0	0	c row
3	6	3	0	0	24	z row
-1	0	3	0	0	24	$z - c$ row
						Basic Variables
$2\frac{1}{2}$	1	$\frac{1}{2}$	0	0	4	x_2 Barley
$\frac{1}{2}$	0	$-\frac{1}{2}$	1	0	8	s_2 Slack labor
$\frac{1}{2}$	0	$-\frac{1}{2}$	0	1	1	s_3 Slack fertilizer

sacrifice $\frac{1}{2}$ bushel of barley (x_2), $-\frac{1}{2}$ man-hour of slack labor (s_2), and $-\frac{1}{2}$ hundredweight of slack fertilizer (s_3). The negative displacement coefficients for s_2 and s_3 here indicate a " negative sacrifice," i.e., an *increase* in the slack labor and fertilizer in the basis as a result of introducing slack land. This may be verified from Figure 5.1 by observing that introducing s_1 into the basis at B would return the solution back along the x_2 axis toward the origin, thereby causing s_2 and s_3 to increase.

Thus the z-row coefficient for s_1 in Table 5.4 is calculated as follows:

$\frac{1}{2}$ bu. of barley displaced per acre of slack land *times* $6 per bushel	$3 per acre
$-\frac{1}{2}$ man-hr. of labor displaced per acre of slack land *times* $0 per man-hour	$0 per acre
$-\frac{1}{2}$ cwt. of fertilizer displaced per acre of slack land *times* $0 per hundredweight	$0 per acre
Total	$3 per acre

Applying the above rules to calculate the z-row coefficient of any of the *basic* variables in Table 5.4 will always result in the answer $z = c$ for these columns. The significance of this will be revealed later. It only remains, then, to recall that we wish to keep track of the total profit earned by any combination of variables. Thus, for the basis containing x_2, s_2, s_3 in Table 5.4, we can calculate total profit in a manner mechanically similar to that used in calculating the z-row values above, but using the b-column values of 4, 8 and 1 in place of the a coefficients used earlier. In this way total profit is made up as follows:

4 bu. of barley *times* $6 per bushel	$24
8 man-hrs. of slack labor *times* $0 per man-hour	$0
1 cwt. of slack fertilizer *times* $0 per hundredweight	$0
Total profit	$24

The total value for profit for a given basis may be entered at the intersection of the z row and the b column. Thus $24 is entered in this position in Table 5.4.

5.4   Two Crucial Questions

We have noted that the simplex method transforms any given basis into any other by a series of iterations, at each of which one nonbasic variable is substituted for a basic one. In the context of profit maximization, the choice of which variables to swap at each iteration arises. Associated with this question is that of recognizing whether a given basis is optimal; i.e., does it maximize profit? These questions can be reduced to two crucial problems. The first is the choice at any stage of which nonbasic variable (if any) should be introduced into the basis at the next iteration. The second is the choice at any stage of which basic variable should be eliminated from the basis.

5.4.1 Choice of the Activity to Be Introduced

In the previous section we saw how for any matrix the c-row value for a particular nonbasic activity indicates the *net profit* accruing per unit to the introduction of that activity *per se*, while the z row shows the *net opportunity cost*, per unit of that activity introduced, resulting from changes in levels of existing basic variables. Let us consider, for any basis, the jth nonbasic variable; call it x_j, call its c-row coefficient c_j, and call its z-row coefficient z_j. Then we can see that the introduction of x_j will be profitable if c_j is greater than z_j—and unprofitable if z_j is greater than c_j. To put it another way, if $z_j - c_j$ is less than zero (i.e., negative), the introduction of a unit of x_j will add more to total profit than it takes away; whereas if $z_j - c_j$ is greater than zero (i.e., positive), the introduction of x_j will subtract more from total profit than it adds.

Thus we calculate for a given tableau the $z_j - c_j$ row as is shown for the nonbasic variables in Tables 5.3 and 5.4. Then in choosing which variable to introduce into the basis, it seems reasonable, since our objective is profit maximization, to introduce at any stage that variable which will yield the greatest net increase in total profit, i.e., that variable with the *largest negative coefficient* in the $z - c$ row. To illustrate, the $z - c$ row in Table 5.3 shows that in the initial basis, x_2 has the largest negative $z - c$ value. It shows that introducing x_2 into the basis would increase profit at the rate of \$6 per bushel (of barley), while introducing x_1 would yield a net increase of only \$4 per bushel (of wheat). Now consider Table 5.4, which contains the basis at point B in Figure 5.1. The $z - c$ row in this table indicates that introducing x_1 into this basis would yield a *net increase* in profit of \$1 per bushel (of wheat), whereas bringing s_1, slack land, into the basis would cause a *net decrease* in profit of \$3 per acre. Thus, for the matrix in Table 5.3, x_2 would obviously be chosen as the nonbasic variable to be introduced at the next iteration; for the tableau in Table 5.4, x_1 would be chosen.

Furthermore we can see that if *every* nonbasic variable in a given matrix has a $z - c$ value which is zero or positive, the introduction of *any* one of them could not increase profit. Hence such a basis would be optimal. Each iteration of the simplex method, therefore, introduces whichever activity has the largest negative $z - c$ value, and the optimal basis is recognized when no further negative $z - c$ coefficients remain in the $z - c$ row.

For *basic* variables, since $z = c$, as we have seen, $z - c$ must always be zero. Hence a basic variable could never be "introduced" according to the above rule. In any case it is of course absurd to talk of introducing into the basis a variable that is already there!

5.4.2 Choice of the Activity to Be Eliminated

The second question is that of choosing which basic variable at any stage should be eliminated from the solution. This may be illustrated by using the initial basis in Table 5.3. We have decided to introduce the nonbasic activity barley, x_2, into the basis. Of the basic variables s_1, s_2, and s_3, which should x_2 replace?

If x_2 were to replace s_1, the new basic variables would be x_2, s_2, and s_3, with x_1 and s_1 zero. The point to which this basis corresponds is B in Figure 5.1. Similarly if x_1 were to replace s_2, the new set of basic variables would be s_1, x_2, and s_3, with x_1 and s_2 zero. This corresponds to point D in Figure 5.1. Finally, if x_2 were to replace s_3, the basis would move to point G. Of these, only one, the first, will keep the solution within the feasible region. The other two, moving the solution to G or to D, will cause one or more of the slack variables to become negative and hence cause the basis to become infeasible.

Thus in selecting the activity to be eliminated, we need a method for keeping the basis within the feasible region. Looking back to the initial basis in Table 5.3, we can calculate the amount by which x_2, barley output, could be increased if each resource in turn were the only limitation on production. For instance, since barley requires 2 acres of land per bushel of output and since 8 acres are available, a total of 4 bushels of barley could be produced if land were the only constraint. Similarly barley requires 1 man-hour of labor per bushel. If labor were the only constraint, with 12 man-hours available a total of 12 bushels of barley could be produced. Finally, if fertilizer only were limiting, 5 bushels of barley could be produced, since each bushel of output needs 1 hundredweight of fertilizer and there is a total supply of 5 hundredweight of fertilizer. These calculations may be summarized as shown in Table 5.5.

It is apparent from Table 5.5 that if the barley activity is to be introduced into the initial basis, land is the most limiting resource, since it permits the

TABLE 5.5

Constraint	Total Supply of Resource (*b* column)	Barley's Requirement of This Resource (*a* coefficients for activity x_2)	Max. Possible Barley Production with Respect to This Resource (*R* column)
Land	8 acres	2 acre/bu.	4 bushels
Labor	12 man-hours	1 m-hr./bu.	12 bushels
Fertilizer	5 hundredweight	1 cwt./bu.	5 bushels

smallest increase in barley output (4 bushels). Slack land, s_1 must therefore be chosen as the variable to be eliminated from the basis. In other words in moving the basis away from the origin along the x_2 axis in Figure 5.1, the land constraint is the first to be encountered. Any movement beyond this constraint must be disallowed because it would cause the basis to become infeasible.

A rule for the selection of the basic variable to be replaced at any iteration can thus be stated as follows: Divide each b-column element by the corresponding a coefficient in the column of the activity to be introduced into the solution. Call the resulting column of ratios the R column. Then the basic variable to be eliminated will be that for which the R-column value is smallest. (In Chapter 9 and also in Chapter 13 we shall consider cases where infinite, zero, or negative values appear in the R column.)

EXERCISES

1. List the basic variables and the nonbasic for all vertexes of the constraint set given in the exercises for Chapter 4. Verify that pairs of adjacent vertexes differ by just one variable in the basis.
2. Calculate the numerical values of the coefficients indicated by question marks in the following matrixes:

(a)

x_1	x_2	x_3	s_1	s_2	s_3	b	
?	5	?	?	?	?	?	c row
4	?	?	?	?	?	54	z row
?	?	21	?	?	?	?	$z - c$ row
							Basic Variables
?	?	2	-2	0	?	11	x_1
?	?	3	1	-4	?	?	x_2
?	?	$1\frac{1}{2}$	0	1	?	6	s_3

(b)

x_1	x_2	s_1	s_2	b	
150	200	?	?	?	c row
?	?	?	450	?	z row
?	?	550	?	?	$z - c$ row
					Basic Variables
?	?	?	0	55	x_2
?	?	1	?	65	x_1

3. In each completed tableau from exercise 2 determine which activity, if any, should enter the basis at the next iteration. Write a full explanation of your choice in each case.

4. In matrix (a) of exercise 2 suppose we introduced x_3 into the basis. What effect would this have on total profit? What would happen if this variable's $z - c$ row coefficient were -21 instead of $+21$? Determine which variable x_3 would replace in the solution if it were introduced. Explain.

5. Suppose the $z - c$ coefficient of s_1 in matrix (b) of exercise 2 were -550 and that it is selected to enter the solution. Which currently basic variable will be made nonbasic?

6. Confirm the answer to exercise 5 graphically. (Hint: construct a diagram with s_1 and s_2 as the axes, with constraints representing x_1 and x_2.)

SETTING UP MORE COMPLEX
LINEAR PROGRAMMING
PROBLEMS

PART II

6

ARTIFICIAL VARIABLES

6.1 Minimization as the Reverse of Maximization

In Chapter 5 a solution method was outlined to handle problems of maximization subject to maximum constraints. We now wish to show how minimization problems may be set up so that they may be solved by an extension of this simplex method. First, however, it is necessary to discuss the relationship between maximization and minimization problems, since this has implications about the way in which we set out our linear programming matrixes.

It is obvious that *maximization* of some quantity is exactly equivalent to *minimization* of the *negative* of that quantity and vice versa. For example, the following lists indicate five values for a variable y and the corresponding values for $-y$:

y	$-y$
3	-3
8	-8
-1	1
2	-2
4	-4

In this simple illustration the *maximum* value of y is 8, the second number in the first column above. We see that the *minimum* value of the *negative* of y is the corresponding second value in the other column, i.e., -8. Similarly the *minimum* value of y in the first column, i.e., -1, corresponds to the *maximum* value of the *negative* of y, i.e., 1.

It follows from this simple fact that the profit equation in a maximization problem can be transformed into an equivalent minimization problem by multiplying the equation by -1, and similarly that the cost equation in a minimization problem can be transformed into an equivalent maximization problem by multiplying it by -1. Thus, for example, equation (6.1a) shows the profit equation from our maximization problem in Chapter 1, instructing us to

Maximize $$z = 4x_1 + 6x_2 \qquad (6.1a)$$

Multiplying this by -1 yields the equivalent instruction in terms of minimization, as shown in equation (6.1b).

Minimize $$-z = -4x_1 - 6x_2 \qquad (6.1b)$$

Similarly equation (6.2a) shows the cost equation from the minimization problem of Chapter 2:

Minimize $$z = 3x_1 + 5x_2 \qquad (6.2a)$$

which instruction can be equivalently written as:

Maximize $$-z = -3x_1 - 5x_2 \qquad (6.2b)$$

It will be useful at this stage to set a standard method for writing down the objective functions (i.e., profit/cost equations which are to be maximized/minimized) and for transferring them to tableau form.

We shall continue to write *objective functions* in their simplest form, as in equations (6.1a) and (6.2a), i.e., according to the nature of the problem under study. In transferring problems to tableau form, however, we shall always express objective functions in maximization form for three main reasons:

a. It will enable us to use a consistent rule for writing the c row of the simplex tableau, regardless of whether the problem was originally one of maximization or of minimization. Broadly, this rule is that *positive* quantities in the c row indicate *profits* and *negative* entries indicate *costs* (or "negative profits"). Thus, as we have seen, the c-row entries for the real activities in the tableau of our maximization example were *positive* (representing *profits*). In setting up the matrix for our minimization problem, on the other hand, the *costs* of cornmeal and fishmeal will be written as *negatives* in the c row (see Table 6.1).

b. It follows that this procedure will enable us to use a consistent rule for selecting the nonbasic activity to be introduced at any stage of the simplex procedure regardless of whether the problem was originally one of maximization or of minimization. This is the rule (discussed in the previous chapter) which states that the activity to be introduced should be that having the largest negative $z - c$ value.

c. It will enable the total profit, or total cost, value (the "criterion value") for any basis to be indicated as the coefficient at the intersection of the b column and the $z - c$ row, with the sign reflecting the rule mentioned in (a) above with respect to the c row, i.e., this coefficient will be positive to indicate a profit and negative to indicate a cost.

This discussion is independent of the nature of the constraint set, being confined to the objective function only. At a later stage (section 8.4.3) we shall see how an inequality constraint can also be expressed equivalently either as a maximum or a minimum inequation.

6.2 Initial Solution to a Minimum Constraint Problem

When a problem contains minimum constraints (and/or equality constraints —see Chapter 8), it must be set up in a fashion slightly different from that outlined in previous chapters for the maximum constraint problems. As an illustration of the setting up of these problems, we shall use the minimization example from Chapter 2. Let us write this problem again, in tableau form in Table 6.1 and graphically in Figure 6.1.

In setting up the *maximization* problem, we began with an initial *feasible* basis, in which all real variables had a value zero. The reason the *minimization* example cannot be set up in this way is that Table 6.1 does not contain a feasible basis, since there is no positive identity matrix present. In other words, setting $x_1 = 0$ and $x_2 = 0$ gives us an *infeasible*

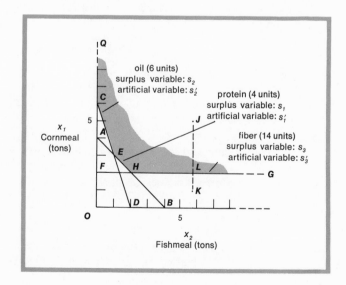

Figure 6.1

TABLE 6.1

Real Variables		Surplus Variables				
Cornmeal	Fishmeal	Protein	Oil	Fiber		
x_1	x_2	s_1	s_2	s_3	b	
−3	−5	0	0	0	0	c row
1	1	−1	0	0	4	Protein
1	3	0	−1	0	6	Oil
7	0	0	0	−1	14	Fiber

solution: $s_1 = -4$, $s_2 = -6$, and $s_3 = -14$. This is confirmed by referring to Figure 6.1 which shows that point O, where x_1 and x_2 are both zero, is clearly outside of the feasible (i.e., shaded) region.

Thus, before we can apply the simplex method to find the optimum solution to problems such as this, we require a means of first generating a feasible basis.

6.3 Definition of Artificial Variables

To create a feasible basis at the origin of Figure 6.1, we introduce a new variable, called an *artificial* variable, for each minimum constraint in the problem. Let us call these new nonnegative variables s_1', s_2', and s_3', and attach s_1' to the first constraint (protein) in Table 6.1, s_2' to the second constraint (oil), and s_3' to the third constraint (fiber). Thus, for example, the equation for the oil restriction becomes

$$1x_1 + 3x_2 - 1s_2 + 1s_2' = 6 \tag{6.3}$$

from which, by setting $x_1 = 0$, $x_2 = 0$, and $s_2 = 0$, we obtain $s_2' = 6$. Adding the three new artificial variables to the matrix in Table 6.1 gives us Table 6.2. In this tableau an identity matrix is obviously present, corresponding to the three new artificial variables. Hence these variables may form a basis. By setting all the other variables, x_1, x_2, s_1, s_2, s_3, equal to zero, we can read off from the right-hand side (the b column) the value of each artificial variable in the initial basis in the same way as we previously read off the values of slack variables. Thus in the initial basis, $s_1' = 4$, $s_2' = 6$, and $s_3' = 14$. A solution such as that shown in Table 6.2 is known as an *artificial basis*.

Technically the basis in Table 6.2 corresponds to the origin of Figure 6.1, with artificial variables measured in the same manner as slack or surplus variables. It is because of the similarity in the method of measuring artificial and slack variables that we have adopted a similar notation for both (i.e., " s " for slack and surplus variables and " s' " for artificial variables). Thus, for example, for any given point (i.e., combination of variables), s'_1 represents the "distance" between that point and any point on the protein constraint AB. To illustrate, we shall use the initial basis shown in Table 6.2. Here we read off $s'_1 = 4$. We could measure this distance graphically on Figure 6.1 as, for example, the length OB, which is equal to 4 tons of fishmeal. With 1 unit of protein content per ton of fishmeal, 4 tons of fishmeal will provide 4 units of protein corresponding to the value of s'_1 calculated above. Similarly, we read from Table 6.2 that $s'_3 = 14$ units of fiber in the initial basis. This can be measured by the distance from the origin to the fiber constraint FG, for example, by the length of OF; this is 2 tons of cornmeal, which, at 7 units of fiber per ton, yields a value of 14 tons of fiber, corresponding to the value of s'_3 noted above. Thus at the origin (the initial basis), each artificial variable is a measure of the distance of the basis from a particular minimum constraint. Indeed, for *any* point in the infeasible region, the values of the artificial variables provide a measure of the "degree of infeasibility" of that basis with respect to each of the minimum constraints.

One might wonder what values to assign to the surplus variables (s_1, s_2, s_3) in an artificial basis. The answer is that the surplus and artificial variables may be considered together in measuring the distance of any point (x_1, x_2) from any given minimum constraint line. With respect to a particular minimum constraint the *surplus* variable measures the distance when the basis is in the feasible region (the artificial variable then considered to be zero). The *artificial* variable, on the other hand, measures the distance from the constraint when the basis is in the *infeasible* region (the surplus variable then considered to be zero). To illustrate, refer to the

TABLE 6.2

Real Variables		Surplus Variables			Artificial Variables				
Cornmeal	Fishmeal	Protein	Oil	Fiber	Protein	Oil	Fiber		
x_1	x_2	s_1	s_2	s_3	s'_1	s'_2	s'_3	b	
-3	-5	0	0	0	0	0	0	0	c row
									Basic Variables
1	1	-1	0	0	1	0	0	4	s'_1 Artificial (protein)
1	3	0	-1	0	0	1	0	6	s'_2 Artificial (oil)
7	0	0	0	-1	0	0	1	14	s'_3 Artificial (fiber)

fiber constraint, FG, in Figure 6.1, for which the surplus variable is s_3 and the artificial variable is s'_3. Point J is within the feasible region and so will be described by a positive surplus variable (s_3), measured with respect to FG by (for example) the distance JL. This distance is equivalent to 3 tons of cornmeal, providing $3 \times 7 = 21$ units of fiber. At point J, therefore, we have $s'_3 = 0$, $s_3 = 21$. On the other hand, a point such as K is *infeasible* with respect to FG, so its distance from FG must be measured by a positive artificial variable, corresponding to, say, the distance KL. This distance is measured as 1 ton of cornmeal, or, equivalently, $1 \times 7 = 7$ units of fiber; thus at K we have $s'_3 = 7$, $s_3 = 0$. Finally at the point L, which lies on the constraint FG itself, both s'_3 and s_3 are zero. It may be easiest to imagine surplus and artificial variables for any constraint as being "mirror images" of each other.

We can now see that any given nonnegative combination of variables in our problem can be *feasible* only if all artificial variables are *zero*. Thus, a method for moving an initial artificial basis into the feasible region suggests itself, viz., transformation of the basis until all the artificial variables are zero. How might this be achieved? The answer is simple. In the matrix in Table 6.2 the artificial variables are *basic*. If we were to transform the matrix successively such that the artificial variables were made *nonbasic*, their values by definition would become zero. Since in one transformation we can swap only one basic and one nonbasic variable, and since in our example we have three artificial variables to remove from the basis, it cannot possibly take us less than three steps to get to a first feasible solution using this method.

Two methods might be used to eliminate the artificial variables from an initial basis. These will be outlined briefly in the remaining two sections of this chapter. The first will not be treated again; the full computation of the second, the so-called "two-phase simplex," will be illustrated in Chapter 10 and developed in Chapters 14 and 15.

6.4 Elimination of Artificial Variables: Method I

The first method is that of "forcing" the artificial activities out of the basis by assigning to each of them in the initial matrix an artificially high cost value or c coefficient. Suppose we assumed that each artificial variable cost, say, $1 million per unit. Then the cost equation which we are attempting to minimize would become

$$z = 3x_1 + 5x_2 + 0s_1 + 0s_2 + 0s_3 + 1{,}000{,}000s'_1 + 1{,}000{,}000s'_2$$
$$+ 1{,}000{,}000s_3 \qquad (6.4)$$

It is obvious that activities as "expensive" as these artificial variables will not appear in a minimum cost solution. Thus the ordinary simplex method could be applied to the initial artificial basis, and we could be fairly sure that s_1', s_2' and s_3' would soon disappear from the solution. Once eliminated from the basis, they would never return, so from that point on they could be removed entirely from the tableau. This method, however, is unsatisfactory from some points of view,[1] so we shall turn to the second method, which is similar in some respects, but which has advantages over the above technique.

6.5 Elimination of Artificial Variables: Method II

This second method involves breaking the solution procedure explicitly into two phases. In phase I we find a feasible basis, and in phase II we proceed from this point to an optimal solution. Let us consider each phase in turn.

6.5.1 Phase I

Phase I begins with the formulation of new rows replacing for the time being the c row, the z row, and the $z - c$ row, which we already have from the initial setup of the problem. The logic of these new rows, which we shall call the c' row, the z' row, and the $z' - c'$ row, is as follows. Imagine that instead of cost minimization, we are seeking values of the variables x_1, x_2, s_1, s_2, s_3, s_1', s_2', and s_3' that will *maximize* some arbitrary measure of "profit." Suppose we assign an arbitrary "profit" of $\$-1$ per unit to each artificial variable (s_1', s_2', and s_3') and a "profit" of zero to every other variable (i.e., $x_1, \cdots, s_3$). Now we can write our new objective as the maximization of a new measure of total "profit," z'; i.e., as:

Maximize
$$z' = 0x_1 + 0x_2 + 0s_1 + 0s_2 + 0s_3 - 1s_1' - 1s_2' - 1s_3' \qquad (6.5)$$

subject to the original set of constraints as in Table 6.1, including of course the usual nonnegativity condition to apply to all variables in equation (6.5). Now, in the initial artificial basis we have $s_1' = 4$, $s_2' = 6$, $s_3 = 14$. Thus in the initial basis total "profit" calculated from equation (6.5) is $(-1 \times 4) + (-1 \times 6) + (-1 \times 14) = \$-24$. It is apparent, then, that we could introduce into the basis x_1, x_2, s_1, s_2, or s_3 without affecting total "profit," since each of these activities has a "profit" of zero. Further,

---

[1] For instance it has proved unsuitable in computer codes.

by *eliminating* s_1', s_2', or s_3' from the basis, total "profit" will be *increased*, since each of these variables has a negative "profit" coefficient in equation (6.5), (viz., -1). The set of nonnegative values of variables which will maximize the new criterion equation (6.5) is therefore

$$
\left.
\begin{aligned}
x_1 &= \\
x_2 &= \\
s_1 &= \\
s_2 &= \\
s_3 &=
\end{aligned}
\right\} \text{Any values}
$$

$$
\begin{aligned}
s_1' &= 0 \\
s_2' &= 0 \\
s_3' &= 0
\end{aligned}
$$

(6.6)

For this combination of values of variables, total "profit," z', must be zero, as can be seen from equation (6.5). Any nonnegative value for s_1', s_2', and/or s_3' *other than* zero would cause z_1' to be less than zero and hence not at its maximum. If, for example, $s_1' = 4$, $s_2' = 2$, and $s_3' = 0$, then z' would equal -6.

In summary, we can see that maximizing z' in equation (6.5) by the ordinary simplex procedure will lead us to a set of values as in equation (6.6). This will represent a *feasible* solution (if one exists)[2], since, as we have seen above, feasibility is indicated by all the artificial variables having a zero value.

6.5.2   Phase II

All through phase I, the "real" $z - c$ row will have been transformed in the usual manner. At the beginning of Phase II the $z' - c'$ row is discarded, having completed its task of helping dispose of the artificial variables. Our attention is now turned to the $z - c$ row. To initiate phase II we inspect the first feasible basis from phase I to see whether it is optimal. This test is carried out by scrutinizing the "real" $z - c$ row in the usual manner; i.e., if any $z - c$ element is negative, the basis is not optimal. On the other hand if all $z - c$ elements are zero or positive, there is no variable that could be introduced into the basis to reduce total costs, and the solution is therefore optimal.

In the case of a nonoptimal first feasible basis, the usual method of solution, as seen in Chapter 5, can be applied, using now the "real" c row, z row, and $z - c$ row to select the activity to enter the basis at each iteration. This procedure continues in the usual way until the optimal vertex is reached.

[2] The case where no feasible solution exists is examined in Chapter 9.

EXERCISES

1. Express the following problems in terms of minimization:
   a. Maximize $z = 32x_1 + 14x_2 + x_3$
   b. Maximize $z = 5x_1 - 2x_2 + 0x_3 + 4x_4$
2. Express the following problems in terms of maximization:
   a. Minimize $z = 7x_1 + 2x_2 + 0s_1 + 0s_2$
   b. Minimize $z = 5x_1 - 2x_2 + 0x_3 + 4x_4$
3. An oil refinery wishes to blend two raw materials, crude oil and semi-refined oil, to produce a minimum-cost fuel, subject to certain minimum requirements on the contents of naphthene, glycine, thyroxine, and listerine. Let x_1 = quantity of crude oil used (in thousand gallons) and x_2 = quantity of semirefined oil used (in thousand gallons). The problem is set up as follows:

Minimize

$$z = 300x_1 + 450x_2$$

subject to

$$
\begin{aligned}
x_1 + x_2 &\geq 350 \text{ (naphthene)} \\
x_2 &\geq 100 \text{ (glycine)} \\
2x_1 + 7x_2 &\geq 1400 \text{ (thyroxine)} \\
10x_1 + x_2 &\geq 500 \text{ (listerine)}
\end{aligned}
$$

and

$$x_1, x_2 \geq 0$$

   a. Explain the interpretation of the objective function (assuming it is measured in dollars) and of each constraint (assuming they are measured simply in units).
   b. Define appropriate surplus and artificial variables, and add them to the set of inequalities.
   c. Set up the problem in tableau form, including the c row, according to the rules outlined in this chapter.
   d. Calculate the z row and $z - c$ row for the initial matrix, using the rules from Chapter 5.
4. In the feed-mix problem in this chapter, determine graphically the values of all surplus and artificial variables at the following combinations of cornmeal (x_1) and fishmeal (x_2):

   a. $x_1 = 1, x_2 = 1$
   b. $x_1 = 5, x_2 = 2$
   c. $x_1 = 1, x_2 = 2$

5. For the blending problem in exercise 3, determine graphically the values of all surplus and artificial variables at the following combinations of x_1 and x_2:

   a. $x_1 = 5$, $x_2 = 0$
   b. $x_1 = 2\frac{1}{2}$, $x_2 = 1$

6. Describe a nongraphical means for deriving a feasible solution to the problem in exercise 3. How would you determine whether a feasible solution so found is optimal?

7

INTRODUCTION TO THE DUAL

7.1 An Example of the Dual

To introduce the important concept of the "dual" problem in linear programming, we shall consider a simple example.

An entrepreneur in a small town employs two men, Jack and Tom, to carve wooden animals that are sold to tourists. Jack fashions the animals roughly out of wood, and Tom finishes off the details and varnishes the final product. Each man possesses skills at his job that the other does not have. They make only three sorts of animals: lions, tigers, and giraffes. Jack, who is willing to work an 8-hour day, carves the beginnings of a lion in $\frac{1}{2}$ hour, of a tiger in 1 hour, and of a giraffe in 1 hour. Tom, who will work for up to 12 hours, takes 3 hours to finish off a lion, $\frac{3}{4}$ hour for a tiger, and $\frac{1}{4}$ hour for a giraffe. The entrepreneur can sell at $8, $7, and $5 each respectively, all the lions, tigers, and giraffes produced. From each of these sums he subtracts $4, 3\frac{1}{2}$, and $3 respectively to cover the costs of materials and his own salary. This means that a lion returns $8 − $4 = $4, a tiger $7 − 3\frac{1}{2}$ = 3\frac{1}{2}$, and a giraffe $5 − $3 = $2 to the input of skilled labor.

The entrepreneur may use one of two methods to choose the most profitable combination of animals. He may set up the usual profit maximization problem, subject to maximum constraints on labor availability. Or, he may set up the problem as one of minimizing his total wage bill, subject to the wage cost of production of each animal being at least as great as the profit on that animal. It may not be apparent that the second approach will give the same solution as the first, but the rationale can be discussed more intelligibly after setting up and solving the problem by each method.

Let us take the maximization problem first. Let x_1, x_2, and x_3, represent the number of lions, tigers, and giraffes produced in one day. Knowing the profit realized on each animal, we can write the total profit per day as

$$z = 4x_1 + 3\tfrac{1}{2}x_2 + 2x_3 \tag{7.1}$$

The inputs of the two men's labor imposes upper limits on the daily output. Thus we can identify a constraint for Jack's labor as follows:

$$\tfrac{1}{2}x_1 + 1x_2 + 1x_3 \leq 8 \text{ hours} \tag{7.2}$$

This shows that if x_1 lions, x_2 tigers, and x_3 giraffes are produced in one day, Jack's total working time will be ($\tfrac{1}{2}$ hour per lion *times* x_1 lions) plus (1 hour per tiger *times* x_2 tigers) plus (1 hour per giraffe *times* x_3 giraffes). This total number of hours cannot exceed 8, because Jack is prepared to work a maximum amount of 8 hours a day.

Similarly a constraint on Tom's working time can be written as in equation (7.3):

$$3x_1 + \tfrac{3}{4}x_2 + \tfrac{1}{4}x_3 \leq 12 \text{ hours} \tag{7.3}$$

As usual we must write

$$x_1, x_2, x_3 \geq 0 \tag{7.4}$$

to exclude negative outputs.

Thus we have a linear programming problem involving the determination of a set of values for x_1, x_2, and x_3 that maximizes the total daily profit, z in equation (7.1), and satisfies the maximum constraints in the inequations (7.2) and (7.3) and the nonnegativity condition in (7.4). We can solve this problem by using in three dimensions the graphical solution procedure devised in Chapter 1. Before doing so, however, let us consider the minimization form of the problem.

The entrepreneur, we now assume, wishes to fix the hourly wage rates for Jack and Tom so that, subject to constraints discussed below, his total daily wage bill is *minimized*. Suppose Jack works his full 8-hour day and Tom works his full 12 hours. Then if we let u_1 and u_2 represent the dollar rate per hour to be paid to Jack and Tom respectively, the entrepreneur's total wage cost for the day, z', will be,

$$z' = 8u_1 + 12u_2 \tag{7.5}$$

First let us suppose that the workers produce only lions. Each lion requires $\tfrac{1}{2}$ hour of Jack's time. Since Jack's wage is $\$u_1$ per hour, it follows that his contribution to the cost of producing one lion is $\$\tfrac{1}{2}u_1$. Similarly Tom devotes 3 hours to a lion, at a wage rate of $\$u_2$ per hour. Thus his contribution to the cost of producing a lion is $\$3u_2$. We can see that the total cost of skilled labor per lion is therefore $\$(\tfrac{1}{2}u_1 + 3u_2)$. We now introduce the constraint that total payments to the inputs of skilled

labor required in producing a lion be not less than the profit per lion, or
$4. This can be written as a minimum constraint, as in equation (7.6):

$$\tfrac{1}{2}u_1 + 3u_2 \geq 4 \qquad (7.6)$$

which is read as follows: ($\tfrac{1}{2}$ hour of Jack's labor *times* his hourly wage
rate) plus (3 hours of Tom's labor *times* his hourly wage rate) must be no
less than $4, the total profit per lion.

Now suppose that the firm produces only tigers. By parallel reasoning
we can derive an expression for the total cost of skilled labor per tiger.
With Jack's wage rate at u_1 per hour and his labor input at 1 hour per
tiger, and with Tom's wage at u_2 per hour and his labor input at $\tfrac{3}{4}$ hour
per tiger, the total wage cost of skilled labor is $(1u_1 + \tfrac{3}{4}u_2)$. We must
introduce the same kind of constraint on total wage costs for tigers as we
did above for lions. Specifically, total wage payments incurred in producing a tiger must be not less than the profit per tiger, $3\tfrac{1}{2}$. We write this
constraint as

$$1u_1 + \tfrac{3}{4}u_2 \geq \$3\tfrac{1}{2} \text{ per tiger} \qquad (7.7)$$

Finally, the minimum constraint on wage rates with respect to the output
of giraffes can be written in a similar way as

$$1u_1 + \tfrac{1}{4}u_2 \geq \$2 \text{ per giraffe} \qquad (7.8)$$

As negative wages are not permissible, we must also write

$$u_1, u_2 \geq 0 \qquad (7.9)$$

Now, if the entrepreneur wishes to produce lions *and* tigers *and* giraffes,
we can see that all three of the minimum constraints in inequations
(7.6) *and* (7.7) *and* (7.8) would have to be accounted for. Thus we have a
linear programming minimization problem analogous to that analyzed in
Chapter 2. We wish to find values for u_1 and u_2 that minimize the total
daily wage bill, z' in equation (7.5), and that satisfy the minimum constraints in inequations (7.6), (7.7), and (7.8) and the nonnegativity condition in the inequation (7.9). This problem can be solved by the graphical
method used in Chapter 2.

What is the rationale of the minimization procedure? The economist
can make sense of the rule "minimize wages subject to the constraint that
wage costs of production are no less than profit" by reference to the
perfect competition model, i.e., a toy industry consisting of a large enough
number of firms, all equally efficient, in which long-run profits are zero
and the whole of the firm's revenue (after paying for materials) is attributed
(or "imputed") to factors (in our example, two types of labor). If the
proportions of Jack-labor and Tom-labor required are fixed regardless of
scale, though different for different products (animals), the resulting wages
of Jack and Tom are determined as the values of u_1 and u_2 that minimize

equation (7.5) subject to the constraints in inequations (7.6) to (7.9). These solution values for u_1 and u_2 are sometimes referred to by economists as the "net product" of Jack-labor and Tom-labor.[1]

7.2 Symmetry of the Dual

By a comparison of the maximization and the minimization forms of the above example, a symmetrical pattern emerges. Let us write the two forms side by side. We have:

Maximize
$$z = 4x_1 + 3\tfrac{1}{2}x_2 + 2x_3$$
subject to
$$\tfrac{1}{2}x_1 + 1x_2 + 1x_3 \leq 8$$
$$3x_1 + \tfrac{3}{4}x_2 + \tfrac{1}{4}x_3 \leq 12 \quad (7.10a)$$
with
$$x_1, x_2, x_3 \geq 0$$

Minimize
$$z' = 8u_1 + 12u_2$$
subject to
$$\tfrac{1}{2}u_1 + 3u_2 \geq 4$$
$$1u_1 + \tfrac{3}{4}u_2 \geq 3\tfrac{1}{2} \quad (7.10b)$$
$$1u_1 + \tfrac{1}{4}u_2 \geq 2$$
with
$$u_1, u_2 \geq 0$$

Notice the following points of symmetry. The coefficients 8 and 12, on the right-hand sides of the constraints in the maximization problem, become the coefficients of the decision variables u_1 and u_2 in the equation to be minimized in the minimization problem, and vice versa. Correspondingly, the coefficients, 4, $3\tfrac{1}{2}$, and 2, on the right-hand side of the constraints in the minimization problem, become the coefficients of the decision variables x_1, x_2, and x_3 in the function to be maximized. Similarly, the coefficients on the left-hand side of the constraints have become transposed; the rows in the maximization problem are set up as columns in the minimization problem, and vice versa. Thus, for example, the coefficient, 3, of the *first* variable in the *second* constraint of the maximization problem becomes, in the minimization form, the coefficient of the *second* variable in the *first* constraint, and vice versa.

If the above maximization problem is called a *primal* problem, the symmetrical minimization problem is called its *dual*. An important result is that the primal and the dual forms for solving a given problem yield the same result. In other words, a set of optimal values for x_1, x_2, and x_3 will imply a corresponding set of optimal values for u_1 and u_2, and conversely, optimal u_1 and u_2 will imply optimal x_1, x_2, and x_3. The maximum profit z yielded by the optimal values for x_1, x_2, and x_3 will exactly equal the minimum cost z' yielded by the optimal values for u_1 and u_2.

---

[1] This concept is distinct from the "marginal product" of each type of labor in a model in which the proportions of the two factors are continuously variable. We shall consider these questions in more detail in Chapter 16.

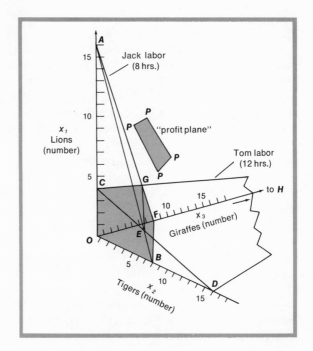

Figure 7.1

This result accords with the model of perfect competition in long-run equilibrium in which the gross revenue (or "profit" in our example) for each firm is wholly distributed as payments to factors of production; in other words, total revenue equals total costs of production. We can demonstrate this by solving graphically the two forms of the above problem. Figure 7.1 is a three-dimensional illustration of the constraint set for the maximization form of the problem. In viewing this figure, imagine the x_2 and the x_3 axes as lying flat on the table, with the x_1 axis rising vertically from the origin. The x_2 axis is closest to the observer. Jack's labor constraint appears as the flat triangular-shaped plane AFB; Tom's is the plane CHD. These two planes intersect along GE. Thus the feasible region is the solid convex polygon $OCGEBF$. The profit plane $PPPP$ (replacing the profit line in two-dimensional diagrams) is drawn "floating in the air" above the feasible region. Moving this plane downward to determine its point of tangency with the feasible region indicates that it would just touch vertex E. In other words, giraffe output x_3 will be zero in the optimal solution, and the optimal vertex will lie in the plane of the x_1 and the x_2 axes. Hence we may redraw the figure, using these two axes only, giving the two-dimensional diagram in Figure 7.2, in which the notation has been transferred directly from Figure 7.1. Thus $OCEB$ is the feasible region, and the slope of the price line PP indicates that the optimum combination

69

lies at point E. We read that this corresponds to values of x_1 just greater than 2 lions, x_2 just less than 7 tigers.

Similarly in Figure 7.3, representing the minimization problem, the straight line FG represents the lower boundary on wage rates in the production of lions. If the $4 profit on lions were imputed solely to Jack, his wage per hour would be $8. If the whole of the $4 were instead imputed to Tom, his wage would be $4/3 an hour. The straight line FG indicates all combinations of wages imputable to Jack and Tom from the $4 profit per lion. The constraint inequation (7.6) requires that the combination of wages paid to Jack and to Tom be not less than those represented along the line FG. HJ is the corresponding wage boundary for tiger production, and LM is that for giraffe production. Thus the feasible region of wage combinations is bounded on its lower side by the vertical axis from infinity to point F, the line $FKNM$, and the horizontal axis from M to infinity.

The slope of the wage-bill line, which represents the quantity to be minimized, is set by the relative *availability* of Jack's and Tom's labors. For example, with a total daily wage bill of $48, if only Jack were employed, working his full 8 hours, this $48 would be incurred by paying him at a rate of $48 ÷ 8 = $6 per hour. This gives point P on the vertical axis of Figure 7.3. On the other hand, if Tom alone were employed, working his full 12-hour day, paying him a wage of $4 per hour would use up the total wage bill of $48. This amount, $4 per hour, gives point P on the horizontal axis of Figure 7.3. Joining these two points indicates the slope of the wage-bill line. Total wages are minimized by shifting this line as

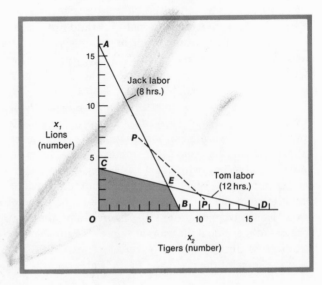

Figure 7.2

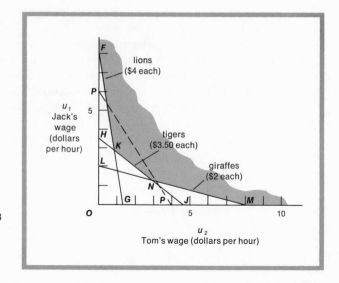

Figure 7.3

close as possible to the origin, at the same time keeping it in the feasible region. The optimum combination of wage rates is seen to be that obtaining at point K, viz., just less than \$3 per hour for Jack and just less than \$1 per hour for Tom.

The graphical analyses above yield only approximate sets of values for x_1, x_2, x_3 and u_1, u_2 at the optimum. We can, however, calculate them accurately. Let us look first at the primal (maximization) form. If we were to add slack variables s_1 and s_2 to the two inequalities (7.2) and (7.3), we would convert them to the following equation set:

$$\tfrac{1}{2}x_1 + 1x_2 + 1x_3 + 1s_1 \qquad\quad = 8$$
$$3x_1 + \tfrac{3}{4}x_2 + \tfrac{1}{4}x_3 \qquad + 1s_2 = 12 \tag{7.11a}$$

with

$$x_1, x_2, x_3, s_1, s_2 \geq 0 \tag{7.11b}$$

Now notice that at point E in Figure 7.2 the labor inputs of both Jack and Tom are fully used. In other words, at the optimum point there is no slack labor, i.e., $s_1 = 0$ and $s_2 = 0$. Further, from Figure 7.1 we see that $x_3 = 0$ at the optimum. Setting these three variables to zero in equation (7.11) reduces this system to the pair of simultaneous equations:

$$\tfrac{1}{2}x_1 + 1x_2 = 8$$
$$3x_1 + \tfrac{3}{4}x_2 = 12 \tag{7.12}$$

Solving (7.12) yields

$$x_1 = 2\tfrac{2}{7} \quad \text{and} \quad x_2 = 6\tfrac{6}{7}$$

The dual (minimization) problem may be independently solved for exact values of u_1 and u_2 in a similar manner. Figure 7.3 shows that the optimum solution at K is unaffected by the minimum constraint on wages in giraffe production, LM; it lies only on the constraints FG and HJ corresponding to lion and tiger profits respectively. Thus we can infer (even if we had not discovered this from the solution to the primal) that giraffe production will be zero in the optimal solution, with only lion and tiger production being rewarded in the distribution of revenue. We may therefore drop the third constraint, (7.8), from our problem, and, with reasoning similar to the above, derive the set of two simultaneous equations:

$$\tfrac{1}{2}u_1 + 3u_2 = 4$$
$$1u_1 + \tfrac{3}{4}u_2 = 3\tfrac{1}{2} \tag{7.13}$$

The solution to this set is

$$u_1 = 2\tfrac{6}{7} \quad \text{and} \quad u_2 = \tfrac{6}{7}$$

Thus from the primal setup of the problem we discover that the entrepreneur should produce no giraffes, $2\tfrac{6}{7}$ lions, and $6\tfrac{6}{7}$ tigers each day in order to maximize his daily profit (all of which, in a long-run competitive model, is absorbed by his payments to the required inputs of skilled labor). From the dual setup we learn that he should fix Jack's wage at $\$2\tfrac{6}{7}$ per hour and Tom's at $\$\tfrac{6}{7}$ per hour in order to minimize his total wage bill.

By incorporating these values into equations (7.1) and (7.5) we can demonstrate that at the optimal points the maximized value of the profit, z, equals the minimized value of the wage bill, z'. From (7.1) we get

$$z = (4 \times 2\tfrac{6}{7}) + (3\tfrac{1}{2} \times 6\tfrac{6}{7}) + (2 \times 0) = 33\tfrac{1}{7} \tag{7.14}$$

Likewise from (7.5) we get

$$z' = (8 \times 2\tfrac{6}{7}) + (12 \times \tfrac{6}{7}) = 33\tfrac{1}{7} \tag{7.15}$$

7.3 Calculation of the Dual Solution from the Primal Solution

The previous section showed how both primal and dual solutions can be calculated independently of each other. But we stated earlier that an optimal solution to a primal problem *implies* an optimal dual solution, and vice versa. We can, for instance, calculate the optimal values of u_1 and u_2 of the dual directly from the optimal values of x_1, x_2, and x_3 in the primal. (In keeping with the general symmetry of the primal/dual problem, we can of course work as well in the opposite direction; i.e., given the optimal values for u_1 and u_2 we can calculate the implied optimal values of x_1, x_2, and x_3.)

Given that the optimal primal values are $x_1 = 2\frac{2}{7}$, $x_2 = 6\frac{6}{7}$, $x_3 = 0$, we may calculate the optimal dual values of u_1 and u_2 as follows: Suppose Jack were to agree to work 1 extra hour each day, i.e., to increase his daily supply of labor from 8 to 9 hours. The equation (7.2) would then be revised to

$$\tfrac{1}{2}x_1 + 1x_2 + 1x_3 \leq 9 \text{ hours} \qquad (7.16)$$

a revision which, in Figure 7.2,[2] would correspond to shifting Jack's labor constraint AB parallel to itself and outward. This would cause the optimum point E to move rightward along the constraint CD, signifying a new optimum combination involving the production of fewer lions and more tigers.

The actual values of x_1 and x_2 at the new optimum position can be calculated as before by solving two simultaneous equations analogous with (7.12). These are

$$\begin{aligned} \tfrac{1}{2}x_1 + 1x_2 &= 9 \\ 3x_1 + \tfrac{3}{4}x_2 &= 12 \end{aligned} \qquad (7.17)$$

The only difference between equations (7.12) and (7.17) is that Jack's labor supply has been changed from 8 hours to 9 hours.

The solution to equation (7.17) is $x_1 = 2$ and $x_2 = 8$. In other words, if Jack were willing to supply an extra hour of labor each day, the entrepreneur should reduce lion production from $2\frac{2}{7}$ to 2 per day and raise tiger production from $6\frac{6}{7}$ to 8 per day. Hence at the new point the firm would be producing $\frac{2}{7}$ fewer lions and $1\frac{1}{7}$ more tigers per day. In value terms this would correspond to a decline in profit of $\$(\frac{2}{7} \times 4) = \$1\frac{1}{7}$, due to loss of lion production, together with an increase of $\$(1\frac{1}{7} \times 3\frac{1}{2}) = \$4$, due to additional tiger production. There would thus be a net gain of $\$2\frac{6}{7}$. Since this gain would be due entirely to the fact that Jack supplied one extra hour of labor, we are correct in referring to it as the "net product" of Jack-labor. This calculation of Jack's worth clearly confirms the value of the wage rate u_1 in the dual problem. It is left to the reader to confirm the value of u_2, using a similar calculation.

Thus the optimum values for u_1 and u_2 are equal to the amounts by which total profit would be increased (or reduced) if Jack and Tom respectively supplied one more (or one less) hour a day. These net product values are often referred to as *shadow prices* or *marginal value products*.

The reader may, as an exercise, use the dual solution of $u_1 = 2\frac{6}{7}$ and $u_2 = \frac{6}{7}$ to calculate from the data given in the minimization problem the values of x_1 and x_2 in the optimal primal solution.

---

[2] Figure 7.1 shows that, under the new conditions, giraffe production will still be zero, so we may disregard x_3.

7.4 General Statement of the Dual

For every primal maximization problem there exists a symmetrical minimization problem called its dual. For every primal minimization problem there exists a symmetrical maximization problem called its dual. For any particular problem it is largely a matter of convenience which formulation we choose to call the primal and which the dual.

To illustrate, we set up below the dual formulations of the maximization example from Chapter 1, followed by the minimization example from Chapter 2. A full interpretation of all coefficients will be discussed in Chapter 16.

MAXIMIZATION EXAMPLE FROM CHAPTER 1

Primal Form	Dual Form
Maximize	Minimize

$$z = 4x_1 + 6x_2 \qquad\qquad z' = 5u_1 + 12u_2 + 8u_3$$

subject to   subject to

$$\begin{aligned} x_1 + x_2 &\leq 5 \\ 3x_1 + x_2 &\leq 12 \\ x_1 + 2x_2 &\leq 8 \end{aligned} \quad (7.18a) \qquad \begin{aligned} u_1 + 3u_2 + u_3 &\geq 4 \\ u_1 + u_2 + 2u_3 &\geq 6 \end{aligned} \quad (7.18b)$$

and   and

$$x_1, x_2 \geq 0 \qquad\qquad\qquad u_1, u_2, u_3 \geq 0$$

MINIMIZATION EXAMPLE FROM CHAPTER 2

Primal Form	Dual Form
Minimize	Maximize

$$z = 3x_1 + 5x_2 \qquad\qquad z' = 4u_1 + 6u_2 + 14u_3$$

subject to   subject to

$$\begin{aligned} x_1 + x_2 &\geq 4 \\ x_1 + 3x_2 &\geq 6 \\ 7x_1 &\geq 14 \end{aligned} \quad (7.19a) \qquad \begin{aligned} u_1 + u_2 + 7u_3 &\leq 3 \\ u_1 + 3u_2 &\leq 5 \end{aligned} \quad (7.19b)$$

and   and

$$x_1, x_2 \geq 0 \qquad\qquad\qquad u_1, u_2, u_3 \geq 0$$

To conclude, we should note briefly important terminology that will be elaborated in our subsequent examination of the dual. So far we have been concerned only with values of primal and dual variables at initial and optimal bases. But we should note that at any vertex for a particular problem there will be a certain set of values for both primal and dual variables. A tableau presentation of a basis contains the elements of both primal and dual solutions at that point. As we have already seen, the primal solution is given in the b column. We now assert that the dual solution is given by elements in the $z - c$ row. If the reasons for this are not apparent now, they will become so later. Henceforth, however, we shall use the term *primal solution* for a given tableau to refer to the values of the basic variables given in the b column and the term *dual solution* to refer to the values of the nonbasic variables given in the $z - c$ row.

EXERCISES

1. From the wheat/barley profit maximization problem of Chapter 1 determine the effect on the solution of:
   a. An increase in land supply of 1 acre (i.e., from 8 acres to 9 acres).
   b. A reduction in fertilizer supply of 1 hundredweight (i.e., from 5 hundredweight to 4 hundredweight).
   Now take the dual of this problem as set out in equation (7.18b), and, using a two-dimensional diagram, determine the optimal values of u_1 and u_3.
   Explain your answers.
2. Write out the dual of the minimization problem given in exercise 3 of Chapter 6.
3. Solve by graphical means the dual of the feed-mix minimization problem of Chapter 2, as shown in equation (7.19b). (Hint: delete u_3 first. Why?) Use your solution to the dual problem to calculate the values of x_1 and x_2 in the primal minimization form.
4. Suggest a method by which optimal values of $x_1, \cdots, x_4$ in the following problem may be found *graphically*:

   Minimize
   $$z = 8x_1 + 3x_2 + 6x_3 + 5x_4$$
   subject to
   $$2x_1 + 1x_2 + 1x_3 \qquad \geq 7$$
   $$1x_1 \qquad + 1x_3 + 1x_4 \geq 5$$
   and
   $$x_1, \cdots, x_4 \geq 0$$

5. Solve the problem in exercise 4. (Timesaving hint: Refer to the exercises in Chapter 4.)

8

MORE ABOUT CONSTRAINTS

8.1 Problems with Mixed Constraints

8.1.1 Minimum Constraints in Maximization Problems

All the maximizing problems considered so far have been subject only to maximum constraints, while the minimization problems have been subject only to minimum constraints on the values of the variables. It is quite obvious, however, that maximization problems may also contain minimum constraints, and vice versa. For example, in the maximization example of Chapter 1, production of wheat and barley was constrained by the availability of three resources: land, labor, and fertilizer. We might also have added a minimum constraint to this allocation problem by specifying, say, that the farmer wished output of wheat to be *at least* $1\frac{1}{2}$ bushels. Recalling that x_1 represents the output of wheat in bushels, we can write this condition as

$$x_1 \geq 1\frac{1}{2} \tag{8.1}$$

This inequation can, after the manner of Chapter 3, be converted to an equality by adding a "surplus" variable; let us call this surplus variable s_4. Then we can write

$$1x_1 - 1s_4 = 1\frac{1}{2} \tag{8.2}$$

where s_4 is, like all other variables, nonnegative. This equation means that the number of bushels of wheat produced (x_1) *less* the number of bushels (if any) by which this minimum restriction is overfulfilled (s_4) must equal the minimum requirement of $1\frac{1}{2}$ bushels.

TABLE 8.1

| Real Variables | | Slack Variables | | | Surplus Variables | | Artificial Variables | | | |
| Wheat | Barley | Land | Labor | Fertilizer | Wheat | Straw | Wheat | Straw | | |
x_1	x_2	s_1	s_2	s_3	s_4	s_5	s_4'	s_5'	b	
4	6	0	0	0	0	0	0	0	0	c row
										Basic Variables
1	2	1	0	0	0	0	0	0	8	s_1 Slack land
3	1	0	1	0	0	0	0	0	12	s_2 Slack labor
1	1	0	0	1	0	0	0	0	5	s_3 Slack fertilizer
1	0	0	0	0	−1	0	1	0	1½	s_4' Artificial (wheat)
2	4	0	0	0	0	−1	0	1	6	s_5' Artificial (straw)

Similarly, in addition to this lower limit on wheat alone, the farmer might specify a joint minimum constraint on the output of the two cereals, wheat and barley. For example, straw is a by-product of both wheat and barley production. Suppose that each bushel of wheat produced yields 2 hundredweight of straw, while each bushel of barley yields 4 hundredweight of straw. If the farmer wishes straw output to be at least 6 hundredweight, the minimum straw constraint may be written as

$$2x_1 + 4x_2 \geq 6 \tag{8.3}$$

In other words, (2 hundredweight straw per bushel of wheat *times* x_1 bushels) plus (4 hundredweight straw per bushel of barley *times* x_2 bushels) must be equal to or greater than a total of 6 hundredweight of straw. Defining s_5 as the surplus variable for this constraint, we can write instead

$$2x_1 + 4x_2 - 1s_5 = 6 \; (s_5 \geq 0) \tag{8.4}$$

Altogether, then, the constraint set for this expanded problem may be written as

$$\begin{aligned}
1x_1 + 2x_2 &\leq 8 \text{ (land maximum)} \\
3x_1 + 1x_2 &\leq 12 \text{ (labor maximum)} \\
1x_1 + 1x_2 &\leq 5 \text{ (fertilizer maximum)} \\
1x_1 &\geq 1\tfrac{1}{2} \text{ (wheat minimum)} \\
2x_1 + 4x_2 &\geq 6 \text{ (straw minimum)}
\end{aligned} \tag{8.5}$$

Thus, incorporating the slack and the surplus variables, the complete problem is:
Maximize

$$z = 4x_1 + 6x_2 \tag{8.6a}$$

subject to

$$\begin{aligned}
1x_1 + 2x_2 + 1s_1 \qquad\qquad\quad &= 8 \text{ (land maximum)} \\
3x_1 + 1x_2 \qquad + 1s_2 \qquad\qquad &= 12 \text{ (labor maximum)} \\
1x_1 + 1x_2 \qquad\qquad + 1s_3 \qquad &= 5 \text{ (fertilizer maximum)} \\
1x_1 + 0x_2 \qquad\qquad\qquad - 1s_4 \quad &= 1\tfrac{1}{2} \text{ (wheat minimum)} \\
2x_1 + 4x_2 \qquad\qquad\qquad\quad - 1s_5 &= 6 \text{ (straw minimum)}
\end{aligned} \tag{8.6b}$$

and

$$x_1, x_2, s_1, \cdots, s_5 \geq 0 \tag{8.6c}$$

The c row and the constraint set for this problem are shown in initial tableau form in Table 8.1. Note the inclusion of the two artificial variables s_4' and s_5' corresponding to the two new minimum constraints. This enables us to form an initial basis containing the three slack variables s_1, s_2, and s_3 and the two artificial variables s_4' and s_5'. Phase I of the simplex method,

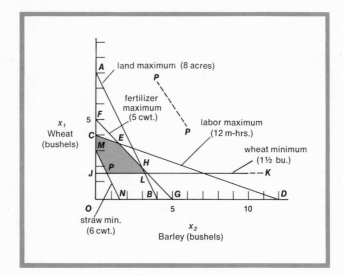

Figure 8.1

as already described, would eliminate s'_4 and s'_5 from the basis, reducing them to zero and thereby leading us to a first feasible solution.

The set of constraints shown in equations (8.6b) and (8.6c) is depicted diagrammatically by the usual techniques, as shown in Figure 8.1. Here the horizontal line JK shows the lower limit on x_1 of $1\frac{1}{2}$ bushels specified by the inequality in (8.1) and equation (8.2). Similarly MN represents the other minimum constraint of 6 hundredweight of straw given in (8.3) and again in (8.4). Remembering that the feasible region was previously $OCEHB$, notice how the new minimum constraints have cut down the size of this area. Combinations of x_1 and x_2, which are feasible with respect to equations (8.6b) and (8.6c), must be within or on the boundary of the shaded region $CEHLPM$.

Recall that the optimum point in the original problem was found graphically in Chapter 1 to be H. It is apparent that in the new problem in equation (8.6) the optimum will still be at H, since this represents the point farthest from the origin to which the profit line (whose slope is shown by PP) could be moved while still remaining in the feasible region. If, on the other hand, the profit line had previously been sloped such that, say, the point B was the optimum vertex, the introduction of the minimum constraint JK would cause the new optimum point to lie at L.

8.1.2 Maximum Constraints in Minimization Problems

In a similar fashion the addition of maximum constraints to minimization problems can be considered. Let us illustrate by using again the simple problem from Chapter 2. Remember that this problem involves the determination of a least-cost combination of cornmeal and fishmeal which conforms to minimum requirements on the contents of protein, oil, and fiber. Now, in ordering the feed mix the customer might also specify a "palatability constraint"; i.e., he might know that if there is more than a certain level of fishmeal in the mixture, say 3 tons, it will become unpalatable for his livestock. This specification then acts as a maximum constraint on the feed-mixing process. Recalling that x_2 measures the number of tons of fishmeal in the mix, we can write this maximum constraint as

$$x_2 \leq 3 \tag{8.7}$$

Adding a nonnegative slack variable s_4 in the usual way, we can rewrite this inequation as

$$1x_2 + 1s_4 = 3 \qquad (s_4 \geq 0) \tag{8.8}$$

This equation specifies that x_2, the number of tons of fishmeal in the mix, together with s_4, the number of tons (if any) by which the total falls below the palatability limit of 3 tons, must equal 3 tons.

Similarly, joint maximum constraints might be specified by the customer. Remember that one of the minimum constraints on this mix is that oil content be at least 6 units, given that cornmeal supplies 1 unit of oil per ton and fishmeal 3 units per ton. As well as this *minimum* constraint on oil content, the customer may simultaneously wish to specifiy a *maximum* constraint on oil content of, say, 12 units. This restriction could be written as follows:

$$1x_1 + 3x_2 \leq 12 \tag{8.9}$$

Defining a slack variable s_5 to represent the amount (if any) by which the oil maximum constraint is underfulfilled, we can write the inequation (8.9) as the equation

$$1x_1 + 3x_2 + 1s_5 = 12 \qquad (s_5 \geq 0) \tag{8.10}$$

Our minimization problem now has three minimum and two maximum constraints. Let us write this complete constraint set, as in (8.11):

$$
\begin{aligned}
1x_1 + 1x_2 &\geq 4 \text{ (protein minimum)} \\
1x_1 + 3x_2 &\geq 6 \text{ (oil minimum)} \\
7x_1 &\geq 14 \text{ (fiber minimum)} \\
1x_2 &\leq 3 \text{ (palatability maximum)} \\
1x_1 + 3x_2 &\leq 12 \text{ (oil maximum)}
\end{aligned}
\tag{8.11}
$$

When the appropriate surplus and slack variables as defined above are included, the complete problem appears as follows:

TABLE 8.2

| Real Variables | | Surplus Variables | | | Slack Variables | | Artificial Variables | | | | Basic Variables |
| Cornmeal | Fishmeal | Protein | Oil | Fiber | Palatability | Oil | Protein | Oil | Fiber | | |
x_1	x_2	s_1	s_2	s_3	s_4	s_5	s_1'	s_2'	s_3'	b	
-3	-5	0	0	0	0	0	0	0	0	0	c row
1	1	-1	0	0	0	0	1	0	0	4	s_1' Artificial (protein)
1	3	0	-1	0	0	0	0	1	0	6	s_2' Artificial (oil)
7	0	0	0	-1	0	0	0	0	1	14	s_3' Artificial (fiber)
0	1	0	0	0	1	0	0	0	0	3	s_4 Slack palatability
1	3	0	0	0	0	1	0	0	0	2	s_5 Slack oil

Minimize

$$z = 3x_1 + 5x_2 \tag{8.12a}$$

subject to

$$
\begin{aligned}
1x_1 + 1x_2 - 1s_1 & = 4 \ (\text{protein minimum}) \\
1x_1 + 3x_2 \quad - 1s_2 & = 6 \ (\text{oil minimum}) \\
7x_1 + 0x_2 \quad\quad - 1s_3 & = 14 \ (\text{fiber minimum}) \quad (8.12b) \\
0x_1 + 1x_2 \quad\quad\quad + 1s_4 & = 3 \ (\text{palatability maximum}) \\
1x_1 + 3x_2 \quad\quad\quad\quad + 1s_5 &= 12 \ (\text{oil maximum})
\end{aligned}
$$

and

$$x_1, x_2, s_1, \cdots, s_5 \geq 0 \tag{8.12c}$$

To create a first basis for this problem we must add artificial variables to the protein, oil, and fiber minimum constraints. Call these new activities s_1', s_2', and s_3' respectively. Then the initial tableau for this problem is as shown in Table 8.2. The constraint set in equations (8.12b) and (8.12c) can be graphed as shown in Figure 8.2. Here the line JK depicts the maximum constraint on fishmeal content (inequation [8.7]) and LB represents the upper limit on oil content (8.9). Originally, with only minimum constraints in the problem, the feasible region was $QCEHG$. Now the addition of two maximum constraints has reduced the feasible region to the shaded area $LCEHNM$. As in the example in section 8.1.1, however, the optimum position under the original price assumptions will not have changed. Point E in Figure 8.2 is still the closest feasible point to the origin with respect to the cost line indicated by the relative costs shown in the equation (8.12a).

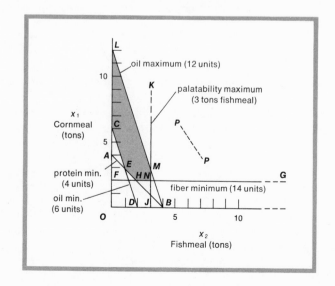

Figure 8.2

8.2 Exact Equality Constraints

Occasionally we wish to specify a constraint neither as a maximum nor as a minimum limit but as a *strict equality*. For instance:

1. In the original profit maximization problem the farmer might specify that *all* the labor *must* be used in the production process, instead of allowing for the possibility that some labor might be slack.

2. In the feed-mix problem a customer might say that no matter how much fishmeal is in the final mix, it *must* contain *exactly* $3\frac{1}{2}$ tons of cornmeal.

The important characteristic of equality constraints is that *they have no slack variable*. Clearly there is no need here to add an extra variable to convert an inequality into an equation, since an exact equality constraint is already specified as an equation. In other words, the notion of over- or underfulfillment of constraints inherent in the slack or the surplus variable concept is inapplicable in the case of an equality restriction, where it is specified that a constraint must be *exactly* met.

The algebraic statements of exact equality in the two examples above are as follows:

1. Given x_1 = wheat production and x_2 = barley production, the labor constraint from Chapter 1, written as an equality, is as follows:

$$3x_1 + 1x_2 = 12 \tag{8.13}$$

This indicates that the sum of labor usage for both wheat and barley must exactly exhaust the 12 man-hours available.

2. In order to specify that a solution to our Chapter 2 minimization problem be such as to contain *exactly* $3\frac{1}{2}$ tons of cornmeal (x_1), we can write simply

$$x_1 = 3\frac{1}{2} \tag{8.14}$$

as an additional constraint to the existing set of three restrictions in our problem.

The complete constraint sets[1] for these two new problems are written (taking the nonnegativity conditions for granted) as follows. Firstly, that for the maximization problem is

$$
\begin{aligned}
1x_1 + 2x_2 &\leq 8 \text{ (land maximum)} \\
3x_1 + 1x_2 &= 12 \text{ (labor equality)} \\
1x_1 + 1x_2 &\leq 5 \text{ (fertilizer maximum)}
\end{aligned}
\tag{8.15}
$$

---

[1] In fact the reader may notice that some constraints in these problems become redundant when the equality constraint is introduced. However, the full constraint set is written in each case for illustrative purposes.

which, when the slack variables s_1 and s_3 are added, becomes

$$
\begin{aligned}
1x_1 + 2x_2 + 1s_1 \quad\quad &= 8 \\
3x_1 + 1x_2 \quad\quad\quad &= 12 \\
1x_1 + 1x_2 \quad\quad + 1s_3 &= 5
\end{aligned}
\tag{8.16}
$$

Secondly, the minimization problem's constraint set is now

$$
\begin{aligned}
1x_1 + 1x_2 &\geq 4 \text{ (protein minimum)} \\
1x_1 + 3x_2 &\geq 6 \text{ (oil minimum)} \\
7x_1 \quad\quad &\geq 14 \text{ (fiber minimum)} \\
1x_1 \quad\quad &= 3\tfrac{1}{2} \text{ (cornmeal equality)}
\end{aligned}
\tag{8.17}
$$

The addition of surplus variables s_1 to s_3 to this problem yields the equation set:

$$
\begin{aligned}
1x_1 + 1x_2 - 1s_1 \quad\quad\quad\quad &= 4 \\
1x_1 + 3x_2 \quad\quad - 1s_2 \quad\quad &= 6 \\
7x_1 \quad\quad\quad\quad\quad - 1s_3 &= 14 \\
1x_1 \quad\quad\quad\quad\quad\quad &= 3\tfrac{1}{2}
\end{aligned}
\tag{8.18}
$$

It is apparent that any constraint set containing one or more equality restrictions will generally not be able immediately to provide a first feasible basis, so that in setting up such a problem for solution by the simplex method, an artificial variable must be added to each equality restriction in the matrix. To illustrate, let us define an artificial variable s_2' to attach to the labor equality constraint in equation (8.16). The tableau for the whole constraint set is shown in Table 8.3. Similarly, defining s_4' as an artificial variable to attach to the equality restriction in equation (8.18), we construct the initial tableau for this problem as shown in Table 8.4. Since *every* constraint in this latter problem has its corresponding artificial variable, we say that the tableau in Table 8.4 contains a *full artificial basis*.

As usual phase I of the simplex applied to the above problems would eliminate the artificial variables from the basis and produce a first feasible solution.

TABLE 8.3

Real Variables		Slack Variables		Artificial Variable		
Wheat	Barley	Land	Fertilizer	Labor		
x_1	x_2	s_1	s_3	s_2'	b	
						Basic Variables
1	2	1	0	0	8	s_1 Slack land
3	1	0	0	1	12	s_2' Artificial (labor)
1	1	0	1	0	5	s_3 Slack fertilizer

TABLE 8.4

Real Variables		Surplus Variables			Artificial Variables					Basic Variables
Cornmeal	Fishmeal	Protein	Oil	Fiber	Protein	Oil	Fiber	Cornmeal		
x_1	x_2	s_1	s_2	s_3	s_1'	s_2'	s_3'	s_4'	b	
1	1	-1	0	0	1	0	0	0	4	s_1' Artificial (protein)
1	3	0	-1	0	0	1	0	0	6	s_2' Artificial (oil)
7	0	0	0	-1	0	0	1	0	14	s_3' Artificial (fiber)
1	0	0	0	0	0	0	0	1	$3\frac{1}{2}$	s_4' Artificial (cornmeal)

Figures 8.3 and 8.4 show the diagrams for these maximization and minimization problems respectively. Originally, when all constraints were inequalities (as in Chapters 1 and 2), the feasible areas in these problems were $OCEHB$ and $QCEHG$ respectively. Now with constraints CD in Figure 8.3 and JK in Figure 8.4 specified as equality restrictions, the area of feasible combinations is greatly reduced in each case. Firstly, in the wheat/barley problem, the constraint in equation (8.13) indicates that combinations of x_1 and x_2 which are feasible with respect to labor *must lie along CD* in Figure 8.3. Further, the existing fertilizer constraint prohibits points to the right of FG. Thus in this new problem the feasible region is reduced to the segment CE. Secondly, the same reasoning applied to the feed-mix problem shows us that the feasible region for the new situation must lie along LK.

As a simple exercise, the reader may apply the original profit (cost) lines to these diagrams, to determine the new optimal solution in each case.

A numerical example containing all three types of constraints—maximum, equality, and minimum—is considered in detail in Chapter 10.

8.3 Constraints Containing " Intermediate Products "

8.3.1 General

A number of production activities provide output that may be used as an input by other activities. Sometimes these "intermediate products" will have no use other than as an input elsewhere in the productive process. For example, imagine an automobile manufacturing company consisting of three divisions: a body division, an engine division, and a final assembly line. Each division uses resources such as capital and manpower, yet the outputs of the body division and the engine division are used simply as inputs into the assembly line. Another possibility is that intermediate products may be put to one of several uses. Imagine, for example, a radio manufacturer that produces its own radio valves. The valves might have a sale value themselves, or they might be used as an input in radio production. In this case the firm is faced with a choice of how to deploy its valve output between use as an input and sale as a product. Yet another possibility is that one productive activity may produce simultaneously output for sale *and* a number of intermediate products. For example, on a farm an oat-producing activity may yield grain for sale, chaff for use in dairy production on the farm, and straw, which may either be used as an input in the dairy enterprise or be sold off the farm.

A simple example will illustrate the nature of these intermediate products. Suppose a farmer has two possible activities open to him, oats or cows.

Let us measure output of oats in terms of bushels of grain and output of cows in terms of numbers of cows in the herd (which will then, we assume, have a direct relationship with milk production). Now consider straw as an input. Straw is used by cows in the same way as the inputs land, labor, and so on, were used by the activities in our earlier production examples. On the other hand the input straw is *produced* as an intermediate product by the oats activity. Let us assume that cows *must* have straw, which they require at a level of 3 hundredweight per head and that the only source of straw on the farm is as a by-product from the oats enterprise, which yields straw at a level of 2 hundredweight per bushel of oats harvested.

It is apparent that the input straw provides a *maximum* constraint on the possible number of cows. For instance, at an output of 6 bushels of oats, there will be a supply of $6 \times 2 = 12$ hundredweight of straw. Since each cow needs 3 hundredweight of straw, this level of straw availability will permit no more than $12\frac{2}{3} = 4$ cows. It is apparent, also, that straw output provides a *minimum* constraint on feasible levels of oats production. If, for example, the number of cows is 12 head, then $12 \times 3 = 36$ hundredweight of straw will be needed. Thus oat production can be no less than $36\frac{}{2} = 18$ bushels, this being the smallest output of oats that will provide the requisite 36 hundredweight of straw.

Letting x_1 = cow numbers and x_2 = oat production in bushels, we can write an equation showing those combinations of x_1 and x_2 at which all straw production from oats is just used up by the cows. Since cows require 3 hundredweight of straw per head, the total straw use by x_1 cows will be $3x_1$ hundredweight. Since each bushel of oats produces 2 hundredweight of straw, the total straw production from x_2 bushels of oats will be $2x_2$. If production and consumption of straw just balance, we will have

$$3x_1 = 2x_2 \tag{8.19}$$

from which we can write

$$3x_1 - 2x_2 = 0 \tag{8.20}$$

Equation (8.20) defines all those combinations of cow numbers and oats output for which the straw output from oats is just used up by the cows. But we wish to allow for the possibility that surplus straw may exist; i.e., oat production can be such that straw produced, $2x_2$ hundredweight, is greater than the $3x_1$ hundredweight required by the cows. In other words we change the equality (8.19) to the inequality

$$2x_2 \geq 3x_1 \tag{8.21}$$

which may be written

$$3x_1 - 2x_2 \leq 0 \tag{8.22}$$

8.3 Constraints Containing "Intermediate Products"

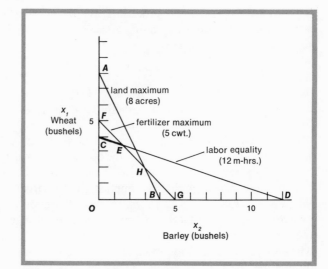

Figure 8.3

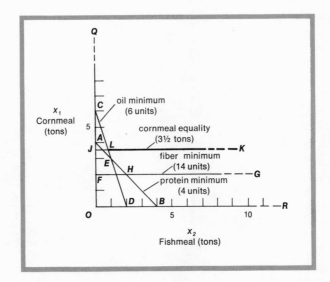

Figure 8.4

Next, by using the familiar procedure, the inequation (8.22) can be converted into an equation by adding a slack variable s_1, defined as slack or unused straw. Thus we have

$$3x_1 - 2x_2 + 1s_1 = 0 \qquad (s_1 \geq 0) \qquad (8.23)$$

which shows that straw used by cows $(3x_1)$ together with any unused straw production $(1s_1)$ must be exactly offset by straw output from oats, $2x_2$.

The inequation in (8.22) can be graphed as shown in Figure 8.5. Here the line OA depicts equation (8.20), the boundary of feasible combinations. The feasible region is bounded above by OA, and below by the x_2 axis in accordance with the implicit nonnegativity condition. The diagram illustrates the way in which this restriction acts as a minimum constraint on oat production as well as a maximum constraint on cow numbers.

Following our discussion of equality restrictions in section 8.2, we may observe the effect of specifying the above straw constraint as an equality rather than as an inequality. This situation would arise if the farmer dictated that the production and consumption of straw must just balance. Such an equality constraint is specified by equation (8.20) above. Specification of this equality restriction rather than the inequality in (8.22) reduces the area of combinations of x_1 and x_2 that are feasible with respect to straw. In Figure 8.5 we see that combinations of x_1 and x_2 that satisfy (8.20) must lie *along the line OA*, whereas combinations satisfying (8.22) could lie along or below OA, as described above.

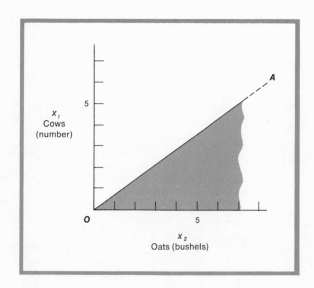

Figure 8.5

8.3.2 Intermediate Products with Inventories

In the discussion in section 8.3.1, the available supply of the intermediate product was assumed to be confined to the current output of the activity, or activities, producing it. This is apparent from, for example, equation (8.23), which shows that the only source of straw for the cows (x_1) is from oats (x_2). A zero coefficient on the right-hand side (b column) of a constraint containing an intermediate product indicates that the only source of supply is from the producing activity or activities themselves.

Let us now consider the case in which the supply of an intermediate product is supplemented from the firm's own inventory stocks. For example, the farmer in the above illustration might have on hand a stock of straw that could be devoted to feeding cattle before any straw need be produced by oats. The "supply" side of our overall balance equation (8.19) must now be augmented by this amount. Suppose the farmer has on hand 6 hundredweight of straw. Then equation (8.19) becomes

$$3x_1 = 2x_2 + 6 \qquad (8.24)$$

This equation gives the number of cattle x_1 that can be fed with the straw produced by x_2 bushels of oats and a stock of 6 hundredweight.[2] Working through as before to the constraint equation, we obtain

$$3x_1 - 2x_2 + 1s_1 = 6 \qquad (8.25)$$

i.e., straw required (3 hundredweight *times* x_1 cattle) *less* straw supplied (2 hundredweight *times* x_2 bushels of oats) *plus* unused straw, if any, *equals* 6 hundredweight. The graph of this constraint (together with implicit nonnegativity conditions) is shown in Figure 8.6. This graph indicates that up to $6/3 = 2$ cows may be produced with the available 6 hundredweight of straw on hand. Thereafter, any further increase in the number of cows can be achieved only if concomitant oat production is undertaken, as indicated by the upper limit EA.

By comparing equations (8.23) and (8.25) we can see that the existence or otherwise of inventories of an intermediate product is simply reflected in the right-hand sides of the equations, or equivalently in the b column coefficients in a tableau. These coefficients denote, as usual, available resource supplies. Thus, if there are no inventories on hand, the b-column coefficient is zero (as in [8.23]), whereas if inventory stocks are present, the coefficient is positive, indicating the amount of such stocks (as in [8.25]).

---

[2] For example, if $x_2 = 3$ bushels, then the amount of straw available is given by the right-hand side of (8.24) as $(2 \times 3) + 6 = 12$ cwt.; at 3 cwt. per head this amount can support 4 cattle, i.e., $x_1 = 4$.

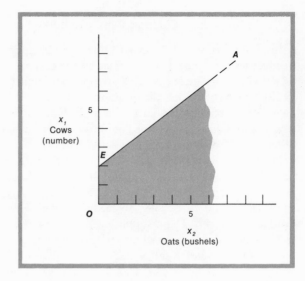

Figure 8.6

8.4 Positive and Negative
Signs in Constraints

8.4.1 Maximum Constraints

It is important to understand the significance of the signs of coefficients in constraints. Take maximum constraints first. To illustrate, refer to equation (8.23). Here the coefficient of x_1, $+3$, is positive, indicating, as we have already seen, that cows *use* or *absorb* 3 hundredweight of straw per head. On the other hand the coefficient of x_2, -2, is negative. This means that the oats activity *supplies* straw at a rate of 2 hundredweight per bushel. Finally any unused straw is *absorbed* by the " slack straw" activity, hence the variable s_1 has a positive coefficient, $+1$.

To summarize, in a tableau presentation of maximum constraints, a *positive* coefficient at the intersection of the column of a particular activity and at the row of a particular resource indicates that the activity *uses* or *absorbs* the resource, whereas a negative coefficient indicates that the activity *supplies* or *donates* the resource.

8.4.2 Minimum Constraints

In a minimum constraint, however, the situation is reversed. For example, returning to our feed-mix problem, where $x_1 =$ tons of cornmeal and $x_2 =$ tons of fishmeal, we can imagine a specification which restricts the *ratio* between the two raw materials in a mix on the grounds, consistency of the mixture. For example, imagine a specifica that the ratio of cornmeal to fishmeal must be *at least* 4 to 1. written as

$$\frac{x_1}{x_2} \geq \frac{4}{1} \tag{8.26}$$

or alternatively

$$x_1 \geq 4x_2 \tag{8.27}$$

or again

$$x_1 - 4x_2 \geq 0 \tag{8.28}$$

Let us add this minimum restriction to the set of constraints in equation (8.12b) by using the surplus variable s_6, thereby converting (8.28) to the equation

$$1x_1 - 4x_2 - 1s_6 = 0 \qquad (s_6 \geq 0) \tag{8.29}$$

If we imagine the consistency of a mixture being measured in some hypothetical "units," we can interpret equation (8.29) as stating that each ton of cornmeal (x_1) *supplies* one "unit" of the "mixture consistency specification" which will be *used up* or *absorbed* at the rate of 4 "units" per ton of fishmeal (x_2). Any surplus "supply" of this specification from cornmeal will be *used up* or *absorbed* by the surplus variable (s_6). For example, a quantity of 8 tons of cornmeal just balances 2 tons of fishmeal, because the 8 tons of x_1 *supplies* $(1 \times 8) = 8$ "units" of this specification and the 2 tons of x_2 *absorbs* $(4 \times 2) = 8$ "units."

Thus, in a tableau presentation of minimum constraints, a positive coefficient at the intersection of the column of a particular activity and at the row of a particular constraint indicates that the activity *supplies* or *donates* units of whatever the constraint represents (resource, feed ingredients, or other item), whereas a *negative* coefficient denotes *use* or *absorption* of the resource, feed ingredients, and so on.

(The reader may, as an exercise, superimpose the consistency constraint shown in [8.28] on Figure 8.2 and solve the feed-mix problem containing this new requirement.)

8.4.3   Interchanging Maximum and Minimum Constraints

The above discussions have revealed that constraints may act simultaneously as maximum and minimum constraints. For instance, in the above illustration we saw how straw output acted as a maximum constraint on cows *and* a minimum constraint on oats. In the algebraic derivation of this constraint in equations (8.19) through (8.23) we treated it as a *maximum constraint*; observe the direction of the inequality sign $\leq$ in equation (8.22) for example, or check the $+1$ coefficient of the slack variable in equation (8.23).

We might alternatively have approached the algebraic definition of this constraint as a *minimum constraint* on oats rather than as a maximum constraint on cows. This would have arisen if from inequation (8.21) we derived, instead of (8.22), the following inequation:

$$-3x_1 + 2x_2 \geq 0 \qquad (8.30)$$

Equation (8.30) says that the amount of straw produced by oats ($2x_2$ hundredweight) must be no less than the $3x_1$ hundredweight required by the x_1 cows. This expression is clearly equivalent to the corresponding maximum constraint in (8.22). Letting the surplus variable s_1 equal the amount by which the minimum constraint (8.30) is overfulfilled, we can derive the corresponding equality:

$$-3x_1 + 2x_2 - 1s_1 = 0 \qquad (8.31)$$

The feasible region defined by equation (8.31) is precisely the same as that defined by equation (8.23) and depicted in Figure 8.5.

Let us summarize these points in tabular form, as follows:

	Maximum Constraint	Minimum Constraint
1. Positive coefficient indicates	Resource used as *input*	Resource supplied as *output*
2. Negative coefficient indicates	Resource supplied as *output*	Resource used as *input*
3. Straw example inequation	$3x_1 - 2x_2 \leq 0$	$-3x_1 + 2x_2 \geq 0$
4. Straw example equation	$3x_1 - 2x_2 + 1s_1 = 0$	$-3x_1 + 2x_2 - 1s_1 = 0$

As we have observed, the two inequations in line 3 are exactly identical, as are the two equations in line 4. Thus it can be seen that simply changing signs throughout a constraint (i.e., multiplying it by -1) reverses the inequality sign; check line 3, working both from the maximum constraint form to the minimum, and vice versa. Similarly, multiplying a constraint *equation* by -1 converts a maximum to a minimum constraint, and vice versa; check line 4.

The fact that a constraint can be changed from a maximum form to its minimum form, or vice versa, simply by changing the signs throughout corresponds to our finding of section 6.1. There it was shown that multiplying the objective function of a linear programming problem by -1 converted it from maximization to minimization, and vice versa.

EXERCISES

1. Add appropriate slack, surplus, and artificial variables to the following constraint set in order that an initial basis may be obtained:

$$2x_1 + 5x_2 - 1x_3 \geq 4$$
$$4x_1 - 2x_2 \qquad \leq 7$$
$$1x_1 \qquad + 3x_3 = 11$$

2. Describe in graphical terms the effects on the feasible regions in two of the problems treated in this chapter if the following changes occurred separately, other things remaining constant:
   a. The straw minimum constraint, MN in Figure 8.1, becomes an equality.
   b. The straw minimum constraint, MN in Figure 8.1, becomes a maximum constraint.
   c. The oil maximum constraint, LB in Figure 8.2, becomes an equality.
   d. The oil maximum constraint, LB in Figure 8.2, becomes a minimum constraint.

   How would these changes affect Tables 8.1 and 8.2?
3. Use the original profit (cost) lines to solve the new problems in (a) to (d) of exercise 2.
4. A tailor who makes coats and trousers wishes to plan his output for next month. He knows that a coat cannot be sold by itself, but that a pair of trousers can be sold either separately or with a coat as part of a two-piece suit. His retail outlet assures him that there is a certain market for 20 pairs of trousers, but thereafter he must produce no more than three pairs of trousers for every coat. If it takes him 2 hours to make a pair of trousers and 4 hours to make a coat, and if he works 200 hours in the month, what output will maximize the number of garments (coats and trousers) produced? Solve graphically.
5. In the problem in exercise 4, what output will maximize the tailor's profit if a suit (coat and trousers) returns him $13 and a pair of trousers alone returns $3?
6. Set up a full initial tableau for the problem in exercise 4. Explain the meaning of the a coefficients in the body of the tableau.

SOME PROBLEM SOLUTIONS

In this chapter we shall examine some special solutions that may occur in the sorts of linear programming problems studied so far. The exposition here will be largely in terms of the diagrams used in the various two-activity problem illustrations in previous chapters. As in foregoing chapters, we wish to understand the underlying logic of the problems studied; therefore we shall outline here simply the means by which these problem solutions may be recognized in the simplex method, and shall reserve fuller computational discussions for Part III.

9.1 Infeasible Solutions

9.1.1 Characteristics

Thus far we have restricted attention mostly to *feasible* solutions to a given set of constraint equations. Let us now consider further the recognition of *infeasible* basic solutions. We shall deal first with the case of maximization problems subject only to maximum constraints. Take again as illustration the simple profit maximization problem of Chapter 1.

As we have already seen, *feasible* combinations of the two real activities wheat and barley (x_1 and x_2) are given by *nonnegative* solutions to the set of simultaneous equations in (9.1).

$$
\begin{aligned}
1x_1 + 2x_2 + 1s_1 \quad\quad\quad &= \ 8 \ \text{(land)} \\
3x_1 + 1x_2 \quad\quad + 1s_2 \quad\quad &= 12 \ \text{(labor)} \\
1x_1 + 1x_2 \quad\quad\quad + 1s_3 &= \ 5 \ \text{(fertilizer)}
\end{aligned}
\tag{9.1}
$$

If *any* variable x_1, x_2, s_1, s_2, or s_3 has a *negative* value in a solution to equation (9.1), that solution is *infeasible*. Thus, as we have seen, any point to the left of the vertical axis and/or below the horizontal axis in Figure 9.1 is infeasible, because x_1 and/or x_2 is negative. Similarly any point to the right of AB and/or CD and/or FG is infeasible, because here s_1 and/or s_2 and/or s_3 is negative.

9.1.2 Recognition of Infeasible Solutions in the Simplex

In tableau form an infeasible basis in such a problem is recognizable by the existence of negative elements in the b column. To illustrate, Table 9.1 shows the tableau containing the basis at point G in Figure 9.1. This combination of no wheat (x_1) and 5 bushels of barley (x_2) is:

1. *Feasible* with respect to the labor contraint CD, which is verified by the existence of 7 man-hours of slack labor in Table 9.1; i.e., $s_2 = 7$.
2. *Feasible* with respect to the fertilizer constraint FG, as this combination of x_1 and x_2 just exhausts the available fertilizer supply of 5 hundred-weight, verified by the fact that s_3 is nonbasic in Table 9.1; i.e., no slack fertilizer exists.
3. *Infeasible* with respect to the land supply AB, as 5 bushels of barley (using 2 acres per bushel) required 10 acres of land, and only 8 are available. Thus the combination at G violates the land constraint to the extent of $10 - 8 = 2$ acres, verified by the existence of $s_1 = -2$ in the basis in Table 9.1.

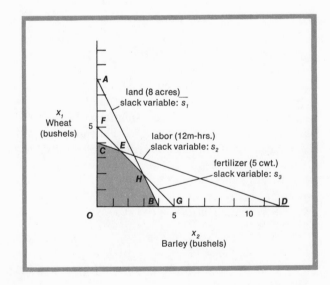

Figure 9.1

TABLE 9.1

Real Variables		Slack Variables				
Wheat	Barley	Land	Labor	Fertilizer		
x_1	x_2	s_1	s_2	s_3	b	
						Basic Variables
-1	0	1	0	-2	-2	s_1 Slack land
2	0	0	1	-1	7	s_2 Slack labor
1	1	0	0	1	5	x_2 Barley

In other words, since *all* variables in a basis are required to be non-negative, the existence of one or more negative variables in a solution indicates that the solution is infeasible. As we have seen in section 5.4.2, the rule for selecting the basic variable to leave the basis at any iteration of the simplex procedure is designed to prevent the solution from straying into the infeasible region. In our example, in moving the solution away from the origin along the x_2 axis, this rule discovers the first constraint to be encountered (i.e., the land constraint AB) and will therefore not permit the basis to move beyond B. Hence, when this rule is applied in these problems, infeasibility such as that described above will not arise.

9.2 Problems Having No Feasible Solution

9.2.1 Characteristics

A more important problem is the recognition of sets of constraints for which *no* basic feasible solution exists. This is of most practical relevance in cases where the two-phase simplex must be applied in order to find an initial basic feasible solution. Let us look at some examples.

Example 1

In the illustration in section 8.1.1 a minimum constraint was added to the above maximization problem specifying that wheat output must be at least $1\frac{1}{2}$ bushels. Suppose instead that this constraint had called for an output of at least 6 bushels of wheat; i.e., $x_1 \geq 6$. The constraint set for this new problem is written as

$$
\begin{aligned}
1x_1 + 2x_2 &\leq 8 \text{ (land maximum)} \\
3x_1 + 1x_2 &\leq 12 \text{ (labor maximum)} \\
1x_1 + 1x_2 &\leq 5 \text{ (fertilizer maximum)} \\
1x_1 \quad\quad &\geq 6 \text{ (wheat minimum)}
\end{aligned}
\tag{9.2}
$$

and, with slack and surplus variables added, the full constraint set appears as

$$
\begin{aligned}
1x_1 + 2x_2 + 1s_1 \quad\quad\quad\quad &= \ 8 \text{ (land maximum)} \\
3x_1 + 1x_2 \quad\quad + 1s_2 \quad\quad &= 12 \text{ (labor maximum)} \\
1x_1 + 1x_2 \quad\quad\quad\quad + 1s_3 \quad &= \ 5 \text{ (fertilizer maximum)} \\
1x_1 + 0x_2 \quad\quad\quad\quad\quad\quad - 1s_4 &= \ 6 \text{ (wheat minimum)}
\end{aligned}
\tag{9.3a}
$$

with

$$
x_1, \cdots, s_4 \geq 0
\tag{9.3b}
$$

The graph of this constraint set is shown in Figure 9.2, the new wheat minimum constraint line being *JK*. We can see that any point in the region *below JK* is now made infeasible with respect to the new wheat minimum requirement. Moreover, any point outside the area *OCEHB* is still infeasible with respect to the three *original* constraints (land, labor, and fertilizer) along with the nonnegativity condition. It follows, therefore, that there can be no feasible point in Figure 9.2 and no feasible solution to the set of constraints in (9.3).

In some cases it is possible by inspection of a set of constraints to ascertain whether a feasible solution exists; in other cases it is not. In either case the simplex method will reveal the true situation, as described below in section 9.2.2.

Example 2

Equality constraints, as we have seen in section 8.6, greatly restrict the area of feasible combinations of variables, and it is again easy to construct

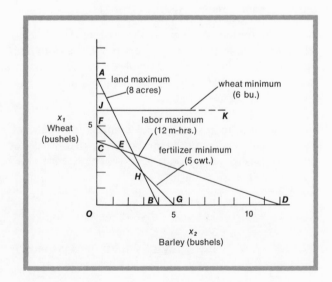

Figure 9.2

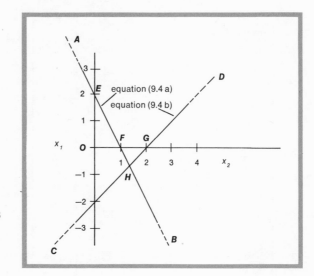

Figure 9.3

an example containing such restrictions for which no feasible solution exists. A simple illustration is the set of two equality constraints shown in equation (9.4).

$$\tfrac{1}{2}x_1 + 1x_2 = 1 \tag{9.4a}$$

$$-1x_1 + 1x_2 = 2 \tag{9.4b}$$

where

$$x_1, x_2 \geq 0$$

In Figure 9.3 line AB represents equation (9.4a) and line CD depicts equation (9.4b). If it were not for the nonnegativity condition, the feasible area would be the point of intersection of AB and CD, i.e., H, where $x_1 = \tfrac{4}{3}$ and $x_2 = -\tfrac{2}{3}$. Once the nonnegativity condition is taken into account, however, the equality constraint (9.4a) by itself will permit only those combinations of x_1 and x_2 which lie along the segment EF, while combinations feasible with respect to constraint (9.4b) must lie on GD. Thus there is no feasible combination of x_1 and x_2 satisfying both equations in (9.4) and the nonnegativity condition as well.

9.2.2 Recognition of No Feasible Solution by the Simplex

In section 6.5, we studied the way in which phase I of the two-phase simplex method finds a first basic feasible solution to a problem containing artificial variables. Recall that at the outset a new c row, z row, and $z - c$ row (called the c' row, z' row, and $z' - c'$ row respectively) are

TABLE 9.2

Tableau 1

| | Real Variables | | Slack Variables | | | Surplus Variable | Artificial Variable | | | |
| | Wheat | Barley | Land | Labor | Fertilizer | Wheat | Wheat | | Basic | |
	x_1	x_2	s_1	s_2	s_3	s_4	s_4'	b	Variables	R
	1	2	1	0	0	0	0	8	s_1 Slack land	8
	③	1	0	1	0	0	0	12	s_2 Slack labor	4 ←
	1	1	0	0	1	0	0	5	s_3 Slack fertilizer	5
	1	0	0	0	0	-1	1	6	s_4' Artificial (wheat)	6
	0	0	0	0	0	0	-1	0	c' row	
	-1	0	0	0	0	1	-1	-6	z' row	
	-1	0	0	0	0	1	0	-6	$z' - c'$ row	

↑

Tableau 2

x_1	x_2	s_1	s_2	s_3	s_4	s_4'	b	Basic Variables
0	$1\frac{2}{3}$	1	$-\frac{1}{3}$	0	0	0	4	s_1 Slack land
1	$\frac{1}{3}$	0	$\frac{1}{3}$	0	0	0	4	x_1 Wheat
0	$\frac{2}{3}$	0	$-\frac{1}{3}$	1	0	0	1	s_3 Slack fertilizer
0	$-\frac{1}{3}$	0	$-\frac{1}{3}$	0	-1	1	2	s_4' Artificial (wheat)
0	0	0	0	0	0	-1	0	c' row
0	$\frac{1}{3}$	0	$\frac{1}{3}$	0	1	-1	-2	z' row
0	$\frac{1}{3}$	0	$\frac{1}{3}$	0	1	0	-2	$z' - c'$ row

formulated in order to maximize a quantity (z') which is some arbitrary measure of "profit." By assigning a profit coefficient (c') of \$1 per unit to each artificial variable, and zero to each real, slack, and surplus variable in the problem, we may use the simplex procedure to force the artificial variables out of the basis (i.e., making them zero). The arbitrary profit (z'), which in the initial tableau is some negative number, is increased to its maximum value of zero at the end of phase I. The reader should refer back to section 6.5.1 if he is unsure about any of these details.

Thus at the end of phase I a feasible solution is reached which is recognized as follows:

1. All $z' - c'$ values are equal to or greater than zero, indicating "optimality" of phase I as measured by 2 below.
2. z' has reached its maximum value of zero.
3. All artificial variables are zero.

Now, *when no feasible solution exists for a given set of constraints*, the following conditions are obtained at the end of phase I:

1. All $z' - c'$ values are equal to or greater than zero, indicating "optimality" of phase I as measured by 2 below; *but*
2. z' has reached a maximum value of *less than zero*.
3. Not all artificial variables are zero.

Let us illustrate this point by using example 1 above. Tableau 1 of Table 9.2 shows the initial matrix representing equation (9.3a), with the artificial variable s_4' added to the minimum constraint. The c' row, z' row, and $z' - c'$ row are shown at the bottom of the tableau; the "real" c, z, and $z - c$ rows are omitted. The largest negative value in the $z' - c'$ row is -1, corresponding to variable x_1; hence this activity is selected to enter the basis at the first iteration. The R column is calculated as usual, leading to the selection of activity s_2 to leave the basis. This swap is performed (the detailed mechanics still do not concern us), and Tableau 2 is obtained. The combination of real variables represented in this tableau (i.e., $x_1 = 4$, $x_2 = 0$) corresponds to point C in Figure 9.2.

Inspection of the $z' - c'$ row of Tableau 2 reveals that it contains no further negative elements; hence no variable can be introduced which will increase total "profit." Yet total profit has not reached zero (it has a value of -2 in Tableau 2), and an artificial variable, s_4', is still in the basis at a positive level, i.e., 2. Since a condition of feasibility of a basis is that it should contain no artificial variable at nonzero level, we recognize that this solution is infeasible.

The detailed computational aspects of the above discussion will be treated in Chapter 14.

9.3   Infinite Solutions

9.3.1   Characteristics

Consider the example in section 8.3.2 illustrating intermediate products with inventories. The problem concerns numbers of cows (x_1) and oat production in bushels (x_2). The intermediate product is straw, and its constraint, given originally in equation (8.25), is of the form

$$3x_1 - 2x_2 + 1s_1 = 6 \qquad (9.5a)$$

with

$$x_1, x_2, s_1 \geq 0 \qquad (9.5b)$$

showing that x_1 cows use 3 hundredweight of straw per head, x_2 bushels of oats supply 2 hundredweight of straw per bushel, and that there is an inventory of straw on hand of 6 hundredweight. Of course, s_1 is the slack variable. We therefore have a problem containing one constraint, together with the usual nonnegativity condition. The area of feasible combinations for this problem is the shaded area on Figure 9.4. Assuming any positive profit for the two activities (say \$3 per head for cows and \$2 per bushel for oats, giving a profit line sloped as $P_1 P_1$), it is apparent that however far the profit line is moved outward from the origin (i.e., in the direction of the arrow) it will still remain within the feasible region. Thus the optimum

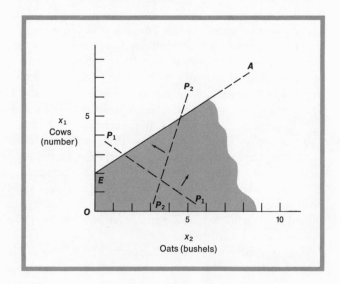

Figure 9.4

solution for this simple problem is at the point where both variables equal infinity. The set described by the constraints in (9.5) is called *open-ended*, and a solution containing one or more variables at an infinite level is called an *infinite solution*.

Of course an open-ended set need not necessarily have an infinite optimum solution. For instance, in the above example, suppose the profit line has a *positive* slope, steeper than the slope of *EA*. This would arise if, for example, cows (x_1) returned \$3 per head, but oats (x_2) had a large negative profit (i.e., a cost). Suppose oats yield \$−9 per bushel. Then we have a profit line sloped as P_2P_2, in which higher profit lines are above and to the left of P_2P_2. Choosing a feasible profit line as high as possible indicates an optimal solution at point *E* in Figure 9.4.

9.3.2   Recognition of Infinite Solutions by the Simplex

The simplex will readily reveal the existence of an infinite optimum solution. Refer to section 5.4.2, where we discussed the choice of variable to leave the basis at any iteration. Remember that we determined which basic variable most limited the activity to be introduced by dividing each *b* column element by the corresponding *a* coefficient of the activity to be introduced. Now recall that in maximum constraints a positive *a* coefficient indicates that an activity uses a resource; a negative coefficient indicates that it supplies the resource; and if $a_{ij} = 0$, the activity neither uses nor supplies the resource. Thus a *positive* coefficient at the intersection of a particular activity column and resource row in a tableau shows that that activity is *limited* by that resource, whereas if the coefficient is *zero* or *negative* the activity is *not limited* by the resource. So if, at any iteration of the simplex when an activity is selected to enter the basis, all the *a* coefficients in its column are zero or negative, we can see that no basic variable limits that activity; it can therefore be introduced into the basis at infinite level and will increase profit to infinity at the same time.

To illustrate, a simple problem is represented in the tableau shown in Table 9.3. The problem concerns a producer of two types of egg powder, A and B, denoted by activities x_1 and x_2 respectively. The resources required are two grades of eggs, A and B, and labor. The entrepreneur runs chickens, represented by activity x_3, to produce both grades of eggs; at the end of the period covered by the program, the chickens are sold.

Numerically, egg powder A uses 3 dozen grade A eggs and 95 hours of labor per 100-pound output, while B requires 4 dozen grade B eggs and 90 hours of labor per 100 pounds. Labor availability over the period studied is 3,000 hours. Each batch of chickens produces 5 dozen grade A eggs and 4 dozen grade B, and uses no labor. Finally, the selling prices of egg powders A and B are \$12 and \$10 per 100 pounds respectively; when eventually sold, the chickens realize \$15 per batch. All this information is

TABLE 9.3

Real Variables			Slack Variables				
Egg Powder A	Egg Powder B	Chickens	Eggs A	Eggs B	Labor		
x_1 (00 lb.)	x_2 (00 lb.)	x_3 (batches)	s_1	s_2	s_3	b	
12	10	15	0	0	0	0	c row
0	0	0	0	0	0	0	z row
−12	−10	−15	0	0	0	0	$z - c$ row
							Basic Variables
3	0	−5	1	0	0	0	s_1 Slack eggs A (doz.)
0	4	−4	0	1	0	0	s_2 Slack eggs B (doz.)
95	90	0	0	0	1	3000	s_3 Slack labor (hrs.)

contained in Table 9.3, and the reader should check each coefficient carefully.

To initiate the ordinary simplex method for this tableau, we select chickens, x_3, as the most profitable activity to enter the basis at the first iteration. But when we come to calculate the R column by dividing each b coefficient by the corresponding a coefficient in the x_3 column, we find all these a coefficients are either zero or negative. In other words, none of the constraints in this simple problem limits the production of chickens, and the entrepreneur's optimal policy is to earn an infinite profit by producing an infinite number of chickens. Of course such a policy arises through poor specification of the problem; clearly, chicken production in reality would be limited by resources not included in Table 9.3.

In many problems whose optimal solutions are infinite, a number of iterations will be required before the existence of the infinite optimum is revealed.

9.4 Degenerate Solutions

9.4.1 Characteristics

We know that a basis may be formed for a particular constraint set from a subset of variables containing just as many variables as there are constraints in the set. Thus, for example, in a problem containing ten variables (say seven real and three slack) and three constraints, a basis containing three variables, real and/or slack, may be formed, and the remaining seven variables must be nonbasic, i.e., zero. In most problems studied so far, all basic variables have been *nonzero* (i.e., positive). Now we must look at a special class of problem in which not only are the nonbasic variables equal to zero, but also one or more of the *basic* variables. Any solution containing one or more basic variables—real, slack, surplus, or artificial—at a level of zero is called *degenerate*.

For example, recall the problem containing cows (x_1) and oats (x_2). In this problem, used to illustrate intermediate products in section 8.3.1, we specified a straw constraint of the form:

$$3x_1 - 2x_2 + 1s_1 = 0 \qquad (9.6)$$

Suppose now we write one further constraint for this problem. Imagine that 5 acres of land are available, that cows require 1 acre per head, and that oats production needs 1 acre per bushel. Defining a slack variable, s_2, for this land maximum constraint, we write the full constraint set as

$$\begin{aligned} 3x_1 - 2x_2 + 1s_1 \qquad &= 0 \text{ (straw)} \\ 1x_1 + 1x_2 \qquad + 1s_2 &= 5 \text{ (land)} \end{aligned} \qquad (9.7a)$$

with

$$x_1, \cdots, s_2 \geq 0 \qquad (9.7b)$$

The constraint set in (9.7a) contains two nonbasic variables, x_1 and x_2, whose values are set at zero in the usual way. We may then read the values of the two basic variables s_1 and s_2. We find $s_1 = 0$, $s_2 = 5$; hence this initial basis, since it contains a basic variable at a zero level, provides an example of degeneracy.

9.4.2 Implications of Degeneracy for the Simplex

The characteristic feature of a degenerate solution is that the introduction of *any* nonbasic variable into the solution *to replace a basic variable whose value is zero* has the following three effects:

1. It will cause the value of the introduced variable in the basis also to be zero.
2. It will not change the values of other variables already in the basis.
3. As a corollary of (1) and (2) there will be no change in the value of total profit/cost (i.e., z).

To illustrate the recognition and effects of degeneracy in the simplex, we shall consider two examples.

Example 1

Let us add to the cows/oats problem specified in equation (9.7), the following profit equation to be maximized:

$$z = 6x_1 + 5x_2 \qquad (9.8)$$

Figure 9.5 shows the graphical solution to this problem: OA is the straw constraint and BC is the land constraint. The feasible area is thus the triangle ODC. With the profit line sloped as PP, the optimal vertex is indicated as point D, where $x_1 = 2$ head of cows and $x_2 = 3$ bushels of oats.

Setting this problem up in tableau form for solution by the simplex yields Tableau 1 of Table 9.4. Clearly the basis contained in this tableau (viz., $s_1 = 0$, $s_2 = 5$) corresponds to the origin of Figure 9.5.

The first iteration will introduce x_1 (why?) and calculating the R values for rows 1 and 2 of the matrix yields $\frac{0}{3} = 0$ and $\frac{5}{1} = 5$ respectively. Thus the variable s_1, slack straw, is selected to leave the basis, having the smallest R value.

The transformation to Tableau 2 illustrates the three effects of replacing a zero basic variable which were mentioned above.

1. Firstly, we see that the value of the introduced variable, x_1 (cows), is zero in the new basis contained in Tableau 2.
2. Next we observe that the other basic variable in Tableau 2 (slack land, s_2) has not changed in value from Tableau 1; i.e., it remains at 5 acres.
3. Finally total profit, initially zero, has not been increased in Tableau 2.

Diagrammatically the basis in Tableau 2 still corresponds to point O in Figure 9.5, as can easily be seen.

The next iteration introduces x_2 and yields Tableau 3, which, by inspection of the $z - c$ row, is seen to be optimal (why?). The new basis

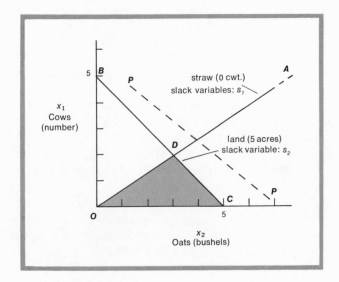

Figure 9.5

TABLE 9.4

Tableau 1

Real Variables		Slack Variables				
Cows	Oats	Straw	Land			
x_1	x_2	s_1	s_2	b		
6	5	0	0	0	c row	
0	0	0	0	0	z row	R
−6	−5	0	0	0	$z - c$ row	
					Basic Variables	
3	−2	1	0	0	s_1 Slack straw	0
1	1	0	1	5	s_2 Slack land	5

Tableau 2

x_1	x_2	s_1	s_2	b		
6	5	0	0	0	c row	
6	−4	2	0	0	z row	R
0	−9	2	0	0	$z - c$ row	
					Basic Variables	
1	$-\frac{2}{3}$	$\frac{1}{3}$	0	0	x_1 Cows	—
0	$1\frac{2}{3}$	$-\frac{1}{3}$	1	5	s_2 Slack land	3

Tableau 3

x_1	x_2	s_1	s_2	b		
6	5	0	0	0	c row	
6	5	$1\frac{4}{5}$	$\frac{3}{5}$	27	z row	
0	0	$\frac{1}{5}$	$5\frac{2}{5}$	27	$z - c$ row	
					Basic Variables	
1	0	$\frac{1}{5}$	$\frac{2}{5}$	2	x_1 Cows	
0	1	$-\frac{1}{5}$	$\frac{3}{5}$	3	x_2 Oats	

contains $x_1 = 2$ and $x_2 = 3$, and clearly corresponds to point D in Figure 9.5. At this point total profit is \$27 (check by summing the individual profits accruing to the basic variables in the optimal solution).

Why could we not go *directly* from Tableau 1 to Tableau 3 in Table 9.4? The answer is that one iteration of the simplex may swap only one pair of variables. Thus, since the basis in Tableau 1 contains s_1 and s_2 and that in Tableau 3 contains x_1 and x_2, we cannot move directly from Tableau 1 to

Tableau 3. Tableau 2, although it does not increase profit, is necessary to set the stage for the movement along OA toward D.

Example 2

Let us now illustrate a degenerate solution arising other than at the *beginning* of a simplex calculation. Suppose that, in our wheat/barley example of Chapter 1, with all other coefficients remaining the same, the supply of fertilizer available is increased from 5 hundredweight to $5\frac{3}{5}$ hundredweight. This value has been carefully chosen as that fertilizer supply which will just cause the fertilizer constraint line to pass through the point of intersection of the land and labor constraint lines. Refer to Figure 9.6, where this situation is illustrated. AB and CD are the old land and labor constraint lines respectively, and FG is the new fertilizer constraint. All three constraints pass through W, and the feasible region is $OCWB$. With the price line sloped as PP the optimal vertex is clearly W.

Now, since this problem has three constraints, at any vertex there must be three variables in the basis. At the vertex W, both x_1 and x_2 are clearly basic, having positive values of $3\frac{1}{5}$ bushels and $2\frac{2}{5}$ bushels respectively. Therefore one of the remaining variables (s_1, s_2, or s_3) must also be basic in order to make up the total of three. But at W we see that all land, all labor, and all fertilizer are just exhausted; i.e., no slack land, labor, or fertilizer exists, and $s_1 = 0$, $s_2 = 0$, and $s_3 = 0$. Hence the basis at W must contain one variable at zero level; it could be s_1 or s_2 or s_3. Whichever it is, the remaining two will of course be nonbasic and still zero.

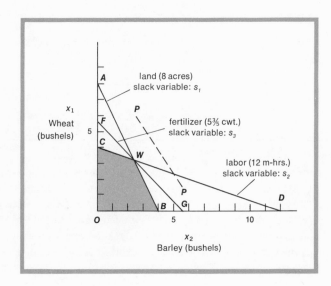

Figure 9.6

TABLE 9.5

Tableau 1

Real Variables		Slack Variables						
Wheat	Barley	Land	Labor	Fertilizer				
x_1	x_2	s_1	s_2	s_3	b			
4	6	0	0	0	0	c row		
0	0	0	0	0	0	z row		
-4	-6	0	0	0	0	$z - c$ row		R
						Basic Variables		
1	2	1	0	0	8	s_1 Slack land		4
3	1	0	1	0	12	s_2 Slack labor		12
1	1	0	0	1	$5\frac{3}{5}$	s_3 Slack fertilizer		$5\frac{3}{5}$

Tableau 2

x_1	x_2	s_1	s_2	s_3	b			
4	6	0	0	0	0	c row		
3	6	3	0	0	24	z row		
-1	0	3	0	0	24	$z - c$ row		R
						Basic Variables		
$\frac{1}{2}$	1	$\frac{1}{2}$	0	0	4	x_2 Barley		8
$2\frac{1}{2}$	0	$-\frac{1}{2}$	1	0	8	s_2 Slack labor		$3\frac{1}{5}$
$\frac{1}{2}$	0	$-\frac{1}{2}$	0	1	$1\frac{3}{5}$	s_3 Slack fertilizer		$3\frac{1}{5}$

Tableau 3

x_1	x_2	s_1	s_2	s_3	b	
4	6	0	0	0	0	c row
4	6	$2\frac{4}{5}$	$\frac{2}{5}$	0	$27\frac{1}{5}$	z row
0	0	$2\frac{4}{5}$	$\frac{2}{5}$	0	$27\frac{1}{5}$	$z - c$ row
						Basic Variables
0	1	$\frac{3}{5}$	$-\frac{1}{5}$	0	$2\frac{2}{5}$	x_2 Barley
1	0	$-\frac{1}{5}$	$\frac{2}{5}$	0	$3\frac{1}{5}$	x_1 Wheat
0	0	$-\frac{2}{5}$	$-\frac{1}{5}$	1	0	s_3 Slack fertilizer

Thus we see that the basis at W is *degenerate*, containing an activity at zero level.

Table 9.5. illustrates the steps in the simplex solution of this problem. In checking, the reader should note particularly that in selecting the variable to leave the basis in proceeding from Tableau 2 to Tableau 3, we come across a "tie" in the R values between variables s_2 and s_3. Each of these constraints yields an R value of $3\frac{1}{5}$. We may thus select either s_2 or s_3 to leave the basis. Choosing s_2, we reach Tableau 3 which contains the degenerate solution $x_1 = 3\frac{1}{5}$, $x_2 = 2\frac{2}{5}$, and $s_3 = 0$. If we had instead chosen s_3 to leave the basis at Tableau 2, we would have obtained an optimal Tableau 3 containing a basis composed of $x_1 = 3\frac{1}{5}$, $x_2 = 2\frac{2}{5}$, and $s_2 = 0$.

Degenerate solutions occur frequently in practical linear programming, but they never seriously affect the finding of an optimum by the simplex procedure. In computer calculation of large linear programming matrixes, many iterations are frequently performed during which no improvement in the value of total profit/cost occurs; this occurrence indicates that a succession of variables at zero level are being removed from the basis. Such an occurrence does not matter from the point of view of optimization; the optimum solution, if it exists, will always ultimately be reached.

9.5 Redundant Constraints

9.5.1 Characteristics

In the setting up of linear programming problems a constraint may sometimes lie entirely within a region made infeasible by other constraints. Such a constraint is ineffective and is dominated by other constraints in the set; it is called *redundant*. For instance, consider again our wheat/barley profit maximization example. Suppose the supply of fertilizer were 7 hundredweight instead of 5. The constraint set would now become

$$
\begin{aligned}
1x_1 + 2x_2 + 1s_1 &\quad\quad\quad\quad = 8 \text{ (land)} \\
3x_1 + 1x_2 \quad\quad + 1s_2 &\quad\quad\quad = 12 \text{ (labor)} \\
1x_1 + 1x_2 \quad\quad\quad\quad + 1s_3 &= 7 \text{ (fertilizer)}
\end{aligned}
\tag{9.9a}
$$

with

$$
x_1, \cdots, s_3 \geq 0
\tag{9.9b}
$$

The fertilizer constraint FG in Figure 9.7 is now rendered ineffective by the other two restrictions, land and labor, which together produce a feasible area $OCWB$.

9.5.2 Implications of Redundant Constraints for the Simplex

Since a redundant constraint plays no part in limiting the area of feasible combinations of activities, its corresponding slack variable (s_3 in the above example) can never be zero, and therefore always remains in the basis at some positive level. In terms of this illustration, at any combination of x_1

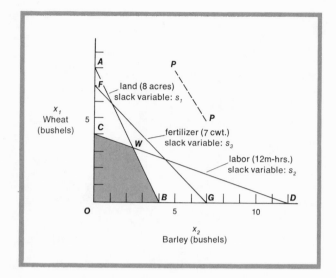

Figure 9.7

and x_2 feasible with respect to land and labor, there will always be excess fertilizer; i.e., slack fertilizer will always exist. Clearly, then, a redundant constraint may be omitted altogether from a set of constraints, since it cannot affect the determination of an optimal solution.

In constructing a large matrix it may not always be possible to determine simply by inspection that a given constraint is redundant. From a practical viewpoint this generally matters little, as a computer will still, of course, find the optimum with respect to the effective constraints in the problem.

9.6 Nonunique Optimal Solutions

9.6.1 Characteristics

We have so far been concerned with linear programming solutions which lie uniquely at vertexes of the feasible region. A problem may, however, have more than one optimal solution. This is best illustrated graphically. In Figure 9.8, which represents the maximization problem from Chapter 1, the line P_1P_1 represents the slope of the profit line obtained when the net profit coefficients for wheat and barley are both, say, $6 per bushel. It will be seen that P_1P_1 is parallel to the fertilizer constraint FG. When this profit line is moved outward from the origin in order to find the optimal solution, we notice that, at the furthest position to which it can be moved, it lies *along* the segment EH. Hence the optimal solution lies not just at one vertex but at two, E and H, and also at any point on the segment of the

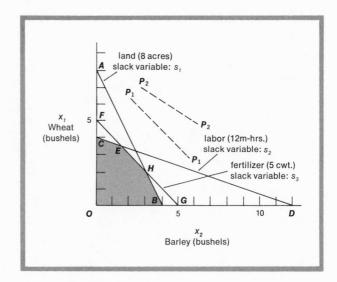

Figure 9.8

constraint joining them, *EH*. Such an optimal solution is called "non-unique." In *n* dimensions (i.e., in problems containing *n* activities) a non-unique solution may lie at up to *n* vertexes of the constraint set and at any point on the $(n - 1)$-dimensional hyperplane joining these vertexes.

It may be confirmed empirically from Figure 9.8 that the profit value of $6 per bushel for both wheat and barley will yield the same total returns at any point on *EH*. At *E*, $x_1 = 3\frac{1}{2}$ bushels, $x_2 = 1\frac{1}{2}$ bushels, hence total returns = $(6 \times 3\frac{1}{2}) + (6 \times 1\frac{1}{2}) = \$30$; at *H*, $x_1 = 2$, $x_2 = 3$, hence total returns = $(6 \times 2) + (6 \times 3) = \$30$; and so on. In other words we can see that moving the solution from *E* down *EH* toward *H* will sacrifice exactly as much revenue from lost wheat production as is added to total revenue from increasing barley production, hence overall revenue remains the same.[1] Similar remarks apply to the reverse movement, i.e., from *H* to *E*.

9.6.2 Recognition of Nonunique Optima by the Simplex

In the simplex the existence of a nonunique optimum in a problem such as this is revealed by the dual solution in the optimal tableau. For instance, the basis at point *E* in Figure 9.8 will contain $x_1 = 3\frac{1}{2}$ bushels, $x_2 = 1\frac{1}{2}$ bushels, s_1 (slack land) = $1\frac{1}{2}$ acres. Zero-valued nonbasic variables at

[1] Reference to Figure 9.8 shows that two other profit lines are derivable from positive profits for wheat and barley which lead also to a nonunique optimum solution. These two other profit lines will be parallel respectively to the other two constraints *CD* and *AB*. In these cases the optimal solution will lie at any point on *CE* or *HB* respectively. It is left as an exercise for the reader to calculate the profit ratios which yield these lines and to verify that the optimal solutions they generate are nonunique.

this point are s_2 (slack labor) and s_3 (slack fertilizer). Now, if the profit line were such that the optimum was *uniquely* determined at E (e.g., the profit line P_2P_2 in Figure 9.8), the two nonbasic variables s_2 and s_3 would both have *positive* $z - c$ values in the optimal matrix. As we already know, a positive $z - c$ value for a particular activity indicates that introduction of that activity into the basis will *reduce* total profit. In Figure 9.8, for instance, with a unique optimal solution at E, the positive $z - c$ value for slack labor, s_2, in an optimal matrix denotes the amount by which total profit would be reduced if the labor constraint CD were moved downward to a point where the overall availability of labor were one unit less. This movement in the labor constraint would move the optimal solution from E down FG toward H.

On the other hand, if the profit line were as P_1P_1, parallel to EH, the tableau corresponding to an optimal point E would now reveal s_2 to have a *zero* $z - c$ value; i.e., labor would now appear to have a zero shadow price. This interpretation is borne out by Figure 9.8, since a unit reduction in the labor constraint, as above, would in this case not affect total profit; as shown in the previous section, movement of the basis down FG from E, when the profit line is P_1P_1, adds as much to total profit as it subtracts.

To illustrate, let us assume that the profit per bushel on both wheat and barley in our example is $6. These profit coefficients yield the line P_1P_1 in Figure 9.8, indicating a nonunique optimal solution lying along EH. Table 9.6 shows the optimal tableau corresponding to point H in Figure 9.8, where $x_1 = 2$ bushels, $x_2 = 3$ bushels, and s_2 (slack labor) $= 2$ man-hours. The nonbasic variables are s_1 and s_3. Observe that the $z - c$ value for s_1, slack land, is zero. It is this coefficient that indicates the nonuniqueness of this optimal basis. It shows that if s_1 were to be introduced into the solution, moving it from H up FG toward E, total profit would remain at $30.

TABLE 9.6

Real Variables		Slack Variables				
Wheat	Barley	Land	Labor	Fertilizer		
x_1	x_2	s_1	s_2	s_3	b	
6	6	0	0	0	0	c row
6	6	0	0	6	30	z row
0	0	0	0	6	30	$z - c$ row
						Basic Variables
0	1	1	0	-1	3	x_2 Barley
0	0	2	1	-5	3	s_2 Slack labor
1	0	-1	0	2	2	x_1 Wheat

Using the terminology introduced in Chapter 7, we call the set of values $s_1 = 0$, $s_3 = 6$ contained in the $z - c$ row of Table 9.6 the "dual solution." We can then see that since the dual solution contains a variable at zero level (viz., s_1), it is degenerate. We therefore say that this tableau contains a *nondegenerate primal solution* and a *degenerate dual solution*.

As an exercise, for cases where optimal solutions lie along CE or HB in Figure 9.8, the reader may list which nonbasic activities at which vertexes will have $z - c$ values of zero.

9.7 Cycling

The phenomenon known as cycling occurs when after a series of iterations in the simplex procedure the solution returns to a vertex through which it has previously passed. Continuing the calculations in the same way as before will merely lead the basis again and again around the same cycle of vertexes, and an optimum will never be reached.

Although this situation sounds like a serious problem, it so rarely occurs in practice that the risk of its happening may be virtually ignored. Indeed, so far as is known, cycling has never appeared in the computation of actual problems, and the only numerical examples available to date have been artificially constructed. Should cycling occur, however, there are means of breaking it, and these have been incorporated in some computer codes, although a number of computer programs do not even bother with the somewhat time-consuming process of automatic cycling checks.[2]

EXERCISES

1. Demonstrate that there are no nonnegative values of the unknowns satisfying the following constraint sets:

   a. $1x_1 - 1x_2 \geq 0$
   $1x_1 + 1x_2 \leq 5$
   $2x_1 + 5x_2 \geq 20$

   b. $2x_1 + 1x_2 + 1x_3 \geq 15$
   $1x_2 - 3x_3 \leq 3$
   $1x_1 \quad\quad + 2x_3 = 5$

[2] Since we shall not return to this problem, the interested reader is referred, for two numerical illustrations of cycling, to: A. J. Hoffman, "Cycling in the Simplex Algorithm," *National Bureau of Standards Report*, No. 2974, December 1953, and E. M. L. Beale, "Cycling in the Dual Simplex Algorithm," *Naval Research Logistics Quarterly*, Vol. 2, pp. 269–275, 1955.

2. Suppose the tailor in exercise 4 of Chapter 8 is *not* subject to any labor constraint. Given that a pair of trousers returns $5, define the range of prices for a coat (*per se*) at which his "optimum" output is infinite. What are his optimum outputs for coat prices beyond both extremes of this range?

3. Explain why the initial basis for the tailor problem in the exercises of Chapter 8 is "degenerate." Which variables will be swapped at the first iteration of the simplex solution of this problem? (See exercise 6, Chapter 8.) What will be the values of variables in the basis resulting from this first iteration?

4. Imagine that the minimum specification for fiber in the feed-mix example of Chapter 2 is increased to 21 units. With other things remaining constant, determine graphically the optimum solution to this problem. List the three possible sets of basic variables (and their values) at the optimum vertex.

5. Take again the feed-mix example from Chapter 2. Suppose the protein specification is halved. What is the significance now of the protein constraint in this problem? By listing the values of basic variables at each feasible vertex, show that the surplus variable s_1 can never be zero.

6. What ratios between the prices of the real variables in the following problems will cause nonunique optima to be found?
   a. The feed-mix example of Chapter 2.
   b. The set of constraints in the problem in the exercises of Chapter 4.
   c. The fuel-blending problem in exercise 3 of Chapter 6.

10

SIMPLIFIED INTERPRETATION
OF COMPUTER SOLUTIONS

10.1 Introduction to Computer
Solution of Linear Programming

The reader should now be sufficiently familiar with linear programming problems to be able to construct simple matrixes, yet he still has not learned all the step-by-step rules for solving them by the simplex method. With the knowledge gained so far, however, the reader should find intelligible the sort of information an electronic computer would provide if it were called upon to solve a specific problem for him.

Given a particular computer, the first essential for the solution of a linear programming problem is, of course, a program of instructions written in a language which the computer recognizes and presented to it in a medium (cards, magnetic tape, or other medium) which the computer accepts. This program will cause the computer to perform a series of calculations on the problem such that an optimal solution is eventually reached. The existing programs for most computers use one or other variants of the simplex procedure as the method of solution. But computers differ widely in size, speed, and flexibility; similarly, different linear programming routines written for a specific computer may vary in speed and in other respects, depending on the skills of the original programmer. Thus a user may consider himself fortunate if he has access to a resourceful program on a fast modern machine.

Just as computers differ in the facilities they offer, so also do they vary in the way they require data to be specified by the user. In matrix layout, for instance, some computers require the initial tableau to be set out with the $z - c$ row at the top; others specify that it should be at the bottom of the tableau. Similarly the b column must be listed on the right-hand side of the matrix for some computers and on the left-hand side for others. Some programs require the whole tableau to be input; others read in merely the nonzero coefficients together with their positions in the tableau.

There is wide variation, too, in the amount and the form of information provided as output from various computer programs. Some provide just the optimal primal and dual solutions to any problem; others list iteration-by-iteration details as well, such as the activities that enter and leave the basis at each transformation. On still other machines, the user may select whatever output he requires; this might range from the optimum only, right up to the full tableau at each stage.

It is therefore impossible to present here one account of computer solution of linear programming problems that will apply to all computers. Instead we shall attempt to summarize some of the procedures dealt with so far by formulating a specific numerical problem and examining what may be regarded as a "typical" output generated by a computer in solving the problem. We shall set up an initial tableau in the manner we have used in previous chapters and assume that this is handed to a computer operator who can translate the coefficients into a form acceptable to our computer. Subsequently the computer output sheet will be returned, and this sheet must then be interpreted. We shall suppose that when solving a linear programming problem our computer outputs the b column and $z - c$ row at each tableau up to and including the optimal one.

To facilitate the analysis, a two-activity problem will be used as illustration, so that the steps in the computer solution can be located on a two-dimensional diagram.

By now we have gained experience in interpreting simplex tableaux even though we have not yet learned all the rules for deriving them. As an aid in the study of this problem the full set of tableaux that would be obtained in a manual solution is presented in the appendix to this chapter.

10.2 Numerical Example

10.2.1 The Problem

Let us take a problem from agriculture, slightly more complicated than the problems examined to date, but still, numerically, highly unrealistic.

Suppose a farmer has two possible activities, cows (x_1, measured in number of head) and clover (x_2, measured in acres) both of which compete for a given 30 acres of land. Imagine that the following constraints apply:

a. One cow requires $\frac{3}{5}$ acre of land, directly competing with every acre of clover (the clover activity used solely for hay and seed production, not for grazing).

b. The farmer's milking shed can handle a maximum of 25 cows.
c. The clover activity produces 15 hundredweight of hay per acre, and cows require 9 hundredweight of hay per head. The farmer has 180 hundredweight of hay on hand. This hay constraint therefore provides an example of an intermediate product with an inventory.
d. Suppose that for reasons of soil fertility the farmer is obliged to have exactly 18 acres of clover—no more, no less.
e. The farmer must use at least 6 acres of land (either activity) if he himself is not to be idle.
f. The farmer is subject to a contract with a local cooperative to use at least 84 gallons of fuel over the time period covered by this analysis. He knows that the milk-shed machinery uses fuel at the rate of 14 gallons per cow over this period, and clover uses 2 gallons per acre for the irrigation equipment.

Given that cows return \$40 per head from the sale of milk and clover returns \$50 per acre from the sale of seed, what is the farmer's optimum combination of enterprises?

We have a linear programming problem of finding nonnegative values of x_1 and x_2 which maximize total profit subject to the set of constraints shown in equation (10.1).

$$\tfrac{3}{5}x_1 + 1x_2 \leq 30 \text{ (Land maximum, acres)} \tag{10.1a}$$

$$1x_1 \leq 25 \text{ (Milking shed maximum, head)} \tag{10.1b}$$

$$9x_1 - 15x_2 \leq 180 \text{ (Hay maximum, hundredweight)} \tag{10.1c}$$

$$1x_2 = 18 \text{ (Fertility equality, acres)} \tag{10.1d}$$

$$\tfrac{3}{5}x_1 + 1x_2 \geq 6 \text{ (Land minimum, acres)} \tag{10.1e}$$

$$14x_1 + 2x_2 \geq 84 \text{ (Fuel minimum, gallons)} \tag{10.1f}$$

Thus we have three maximum constraints, shown in (a) to (c), one equality in (d), and two minimum constraints, (e) and (f). Adding appropriate slack, surplus, and artificial variables, we set the problem out in full as follows:

Maximize

$$z = 40x_1 + 50x_2 \tag{10.2a}$$

subject to

$$
\begin{aligned}
\tfrac{3}{5}x_1 + 1x_2 + 1s_1 &&&&&&& = 30 \\
1x_1 && + 1s_2 &&&&& = 25 \\
9x_1 - 15x_2 && + 1s_3 &&&&& = 180 \tag{10.2b} \\
1x_2 &&&& + 1s_4' &&& = 18 \\
\tfrac{3}{5}x_1 + 1x_2 &&&& - 1s_5 + 1s_5' && = 6 \\
14x_1 + 2x_2 &&&&& - 1s_6 + 1s_6' &= 84
\end{aligned}
$$

and

$$x_1, x_2, s_1, \cdots, s_6' \geq 0 \qquad (10.2c)$$

The reader should carefully compare the construction of this set of equations with the data given above.

10.2.2 Graphical Solution

Figure 10.1 shows a graphical representation of the constraint set for this problem. Table 10.1 lists the constraints and can be used as an aid in interpreting equations (10.1), (10.2), and Figure 10.1.

As the reader may already have realized, solving this problem is rather simpler than appears at first glance, as several of the constraints are redundant. We see that constraint (d) dictates exactly 18 acres of clover; therefore according to constraint (a) 12 acres will be left for cows; at $\frac{3}{5}$ acre per head 20 cows can be carried. It will pay to carry cows in this problem if their profit per head is anything greater than zero; further, we can verify that a combination of $x_1 = 20$ head and $x_2 = 18$ acres satisfies

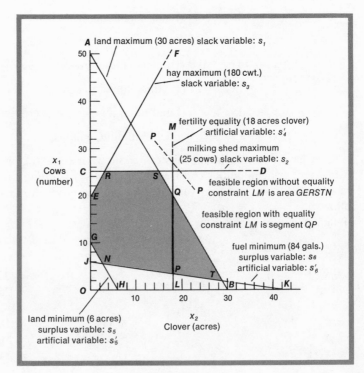

Figure 10.1

TABLE 10.1

Constraint	Type	Slack Variable	Surplus Variable	Artificial Variable	Line on Figure 10.1
Land	Maximum	s_1	—	—	AB
Milking shed	Maximum	s_2	—	—	CD
Hay	Maximum	s_3	—	—	EF
Fertility	Equality	—	—	s_4'	LM
Land	Minimum	—	s_5	s_5'	GH
Fuel	Minimum	—	s_6	s_6'	JK

all other constraints besides (a) and (d); hence this solution is optimal and feasible.

Referring to Figure 10.1 we notice that with the exclusion of the equality restriction (d), the maximum and the minimum constraints would give a feasible area of *GERSTN*. However, the addition of the equality restriction *LM* reduces the area of feasibility to any point along the segment *PQ*. With the profit line sloped as *PP* in the figure, we can readily see that the optimum solution lies at *Q*, verifying the solution found above of $x_1 = 20$ head of cows, $x_2 = 18$ acres of clover.

Despite redundancy, for illustrative purposes we carry the full set of constraints throughout.

10.3 Computer Solution

10.3.1 Initial Tableau

Following our customary procedures the initial tableau is set up in Table 10.2. The c row at the top of the tableau represents the profits accruing to each activity; only the "real" activities x_1 and x_2 have nonzero coefficients in this row. At the bottom of the tableau, in the c' row we see the arbitrary "profit" coefficients designed to eliminate the artificial variables in phase I of the simplex. All real, slack, and surplus variables have zero "profits," while the artificial variables have c'-row coefficients of -1. This ensures that the artificial variables will disappear from the basis during phase I if a feasible solution to the problem exists. We have not yet dealt with the calculation of the z' and $z' - c'$ rows, so the reader may ignore them at this stage.

Remember that in the setup of a linear programming matrix the order of rows and columns is immaterial; in Table 10.2 the maximum constraint slack variables and the artificial variables have been grouped together in order that the identity matrix formed by their columns will appear as a neat diagonal row of 1's.

TABLE 10.2

	Real Variables		Surplus Variables		Slack Variables			Artificial Variables				Basic Variables
	Cows x_1 (head)	Clover x_2 (acres)	Land s_5 (acres)	Fuel s_6 (gals.)	Land s_1 (acres)	Milking shed s_2 (head)	Hay s_3 (cwt.)	Fertility s_4' (acres)	Land s_5' (acres)	Fuel s_6' (gals.)	b	
	40	50	0	0	0	0	0	0	0	0	0	c row
	0	0	0	0	0	0	0	0	0	0	0	z row
	−40	−50	0	0	0	0	0	0	0	0	0	$z - c$ row
	0.6	1	0	0	1	0	0	0	0	0	30	s_1 Slack land
	1	0	0	0	0	1	0	0	0	0	25	s_2 Slack shed
	9	−15	0	0	0	0	1	0	0	0	180	s_3 Slack hay
	0	1	0	0	0	0	0	1	0	0	18	s_4' Artificial (fertility)
	0.6	1	−1	0	0	0	0	0	1	0	6	s_5' Artificial (land)
	14	2	0	−1	0	0	0	0	0	1	84	s_6' Artificial (fuel)
	0	0	0	0	0	0	0	−1	−1	−1	0	c' row
	−14.6	−4	1	1	0	0	0	−1	−1	−1	−108	z' row
	−14.6	−4	1	1	0	0	0	0	0	0	−108	$z' - c'$ row

124

10.3.2 Interpretation of Calculation Procedure

After handing the tableau in Table 10.2 over to the operator, we wait for the output sheet to come from the computer when the calculations are finished. As mentioned above, we assume that our computer lists the primal and the dual solutions at each tableau. In other words we obtain, for each tableau (i.e., at each vertex through which the solution passes) a list of basic activities together with their b-column values (the primal solution at that vertex) and a list of nonbasic activities together with their $z - c$ row values (the dual solution at that vertex). Table 10.2 shows that altogether we have ten activities (real, surplus, slack, and artificial) and six constraints. Therefore at any vertex we will have six activities in the basis and hence $10 - 6 = 4$ nonbasic activities (at zero level).

Table 10.3 shows the information received from the computer. Examination of the sequence of tableaux shown in this table enables us to identify which activities enter and leave the basis at each stage. Thus, for instance, in moving from Tableau 1 to Tableau 2 we see that x_1, the cows activity, becomes basic, replacing s_6', the fuel minimum artificial, which becomes nonbasic in Tableau 2. Further, knowing the variables in the basis at each tableau enables us to identify the vertex on Figure 10.1 to which each tableau corresponds. Table 10.4, then, shows iteration-by-iteration details of activities entering and leaving the basis and traces the path followed by the solution on Figure 10.1.

Let us examine the solution sequence in more detail. Tableau 1 shows the initial basis and corresponds to the matrix shown in Table 10.2. The first iteration, using the $z' - c'$ row to make the selection, chooses x_1 to enter the basis, replacing s_6', the artificial activity which corresponds to the fuel minimum constraint. This takes us from O to J on Figure 10.1. (The reader should verify at each stage the values of the basic variables in terms of Figure 10.1.) At Tableau 2 there are still two artificial variables (s_4' and s_5') in the basis at nonzero level, so we realize that the solution is still infeasible. Introduction of clover, x_2, at iteration 2 moves us from J down JK to N. Clover enters the basis at a level of 2.63 acres, causing the level of the cows activity x_1 in the solution to fall from 6 head (Tableau 2) to 5.63 head (Tableau 3).

Note that a computer will normally give a large number of decimal places—maybe 10 or 15 digits—for each coefficient in its numerical output. The figures in Table 10.3 have been rounded to the nearest one or two decimal places, and in checking these figures the reader might come across examples of apparent errors introduced by this rounding process. For instance, notice that the $z - c$-row coefficient for x_2 (clover) in Tableau 2 tells us that each acre introduced into the basis would add \$44.29 net to total profit. Thus we might calculate that introduction of

TABLE 10.3

Basic Variables				Nonbasic Variables		
Activity		b-column value		Activity		$z - c$-row value

Tableau 1

s_1	Slack land	30	acres	x_1	Cows	\$ − 40/head
s_2	Slack milking shed	25	head	x_2	Clover	\$ − 50/acre
s_3	Slack hay	180	cwt.	s_5	Surplus land	\$ 0/acre
s_4'	Artificial (fertility)	18	acres	s_6	Surplus fuel	\$ 0/gal.
s_5'	Artificial (land)	6	acres			
s_6'	Artificial (fuel)	84	gals.		TOTAL PROFIT	\$ 0

Tableau 2

s_1	Slack land	26.4	acres	x_2	Clover	\$ − 44.29/acre
s_2	Slack milking shed	19	head	s_5	Surplus land	\$ 0/acre
s_3	Slack hay	126	cwt.	s_6	Surplus fuel	\$ − 2.86/gal
s_4'	Artificial (fertility)	18	acres	s_6'	Artificial (fuel)	\$ 0/gal.
s_5'	Artificial (land)	2.4	acres			
x_1	Cows	6	head		TOTAL PROFIT	\$240

Tableau 3

s_1	Slack land	24.00	acres	s_5	Surplus land	\$ − 48.44/acre
s_2	Slack milking shed	19.38	head	s_6	Surplus fuel	\$ − 0.78/gal.
s_3	Slack hay	168.75	cwt.	s_5'	Artificial (land)	\$ 0/acre
s_4'	Artificial (fertility)	15.38	acres	s_6'	Artificial (fuel)	\$ 0/gal.
x_2	Clover	2.63	acres			
x_1	Cows	5.63	head		TOTAL PROFIT	\$356.25

End of phase I

Tableau 4

s_1	Slack land	9.94	acres	s_6	Surplus fuel	\$ − 2.86/gal.
s_2	Slack milking shed	21.57	head	s_4'	Artificial (fertility)	\$ − 44.29/acre
s_3	Slack hay	419.14	cwt.	s_5'	Artificial (land)	\$ 0/acre
s_5	Surplus land	14.06	acres	s_6'	Artificial (fuel)	\$ 0/gal.
x_2	Clover	18.00	acres			
x_1	Cows	3.43	head		TOTAL PROFIT	\$1,037.14

Tableau 5

s_6	Surplus fuel	232	gals.	s_1	Slack land	\$66.67/acre
s_2	Slack milking shed	5	head	s_4'	Artificial (fertility)	\$ − 16.67/acre
s_3	Slack hay	270	cwt.	s_5'	Artificial (land)	\$ 0/acre
s_5	Surplus land	24	acres	s_6'	Artificial (fuel)	\$ 0/gal.
x_2	Clover	18	acres			
x_1	Cows	20	head		TOTAL PROFIT	\$1,700.00

TABLE 10.4

Iteration Number	Movement in Table 10.3	Variable to Enter Basis	Variable to Leave Basis	Movement on Figure 10.1
1	Tableau 1 to Tableau 2	x_1	s_6'	O to J
2	Tableau 2 to Tableau 3	x_2	s_5'	J to N
3	Tableau 3 to Tableau 4	s_4	s_4'	N to P
4	Tableau 4 to Tableau 5	s_5	s_1	P to Q

2.63 acres of clover in moving through iteration 2 will cause an increase of $44.29 \times 2.63 = \$116.48$ in total profit. Since the total profit at Tableau 2 is \$240, we would conclude that total profit in Tableau 3 should be $\$240 + 116.48 = \$356.48$, whereas the computer output for Tableau 3 specifies this as \$356.25. Our check has gone astray because of rounding errors: the *true* $z - c$ value for x_2 in Tableau 2 is, in fact, \$44.2857143 and the b-column value for x_2 in Tableau 3, also to seven decimal places, is 2.6250000 acres. When multiplied, these two seven-place figures yield a value for the increase in profit of \$116.2500000, verifying exactly the Tableau 3 total of \$356.25 found by the computer.

By the time Tableau 3 is reached, there remains in the basis only one artificial activity, s_4', corresponding to the fertility equality constraint. Iteration 3, moving the solution from Tableau 3 to Tableau 4, removes this activity from the basis, replacing it with s_5, the surplus variable attached to the land minimum constraint. This moves the solution from N down JK to P in Figure 10.2. No further artificial variables are left in the basis at Tableau 4, and the computer prints out the news that phase I has ended and the first feasible solution found. The reader may verify this by observing, in the full tableau presentation in the appendix to this chapter, that at Tableau 4 all $z' - c'$ values are zero, and the value of the "artificial criterion," z', has also reached its maximum value of zero; thus the conditions obtain for the existence of a feasible solution.

Note that in manual calculations we may discard from the tableau the column corresponding to each artificial variable as it leaves the basis, since it must never be selected to reenter the solution. However, the $z - c$ values for the artificial variables are still listed in Table 10.3, as they are necessary for the dual solution checks to be discussed below.

At the end of phase I the tableau of the first feasible basis is inspected (Tableau 4) to ascertain whether it is optimal. Its $z - c$ row indicates that every gallon of the fuel minimum surplus activity introduced into the basis will add \$2.86 to total profit. Introduction of this variable, s_6, will move the solution up LM from P toward Q. Tableau 5 shows the basis at Q. The $z - c$ row of this tableau indicates that no real, slack, or surplus activity can be introduced into the basis to increase profit, hence this basis is optimal. Note that the $z - c$ row *does* contain a negative element,

$\$-16.67$, and at first glance we might conclude that the basis is nonoptimal. On closer inspection, however, we observe that this coefficient belongs to an artificial variable, s_4', and therefore cannot be a candidate for entry into the basis. This artificial variable corresponds to the fertility equality constraint. Introducing it would certainly increase profit, *but* it would cause the solution to become infeasible with respect to the equality restriction; i.e., the value of x_2 in the basis would *change* from 18 acres and would thus violate constraint (d) in equation (10.1). (In terms of Figure 10.1 the introduction of this artificial variable s_4' would cause the basis to move away from Q along AB, toward either S or T, depending on which activity were chosen to leave the basis; if s_2 were chosen the basis would move to S; if s_5 were chosen, it would move to T.)

10.4 Interpretation of the Optimal Solution

10.4.1 Constraint Checks

The values of the basic variables shown in Tableau 5 (or indeed in any preceding tableau) may be checked with respect to the original constraints. For example, we know that total land use in the optimal program is 18 acres for clover *plus* $20 \times \frac{3}{5} = 12$ acres for cows. This gives a total of 30 acres, just exhausting the original supply. We therefore expect to find the land maximum constraint slack variable (s_1) to be *nonbasic* in the final tableau; i.e., no slack land exists at this combination of the real activities. Again, one original minimum requirement was that at least 6 acres of land be used; a land use of 30 acres, as in the optimal solution, exceeds this minimum requirement by $30 - 6 = 24$ acres. Thus we verify the value of the surplus variable (s_5) for the land minimum constraint in Tableau 5; i.e., the value of this variable in the basis shows by how much the minimum constraint is overfulfilled in this solution. As another illustration we note that the milking-shed capacity of 25 head is underfulfilled by 5

TABLE 10.5

	Use of Real Activities		Slack or	Total Resource
Constraint	Cows	Pasture	Surplus	Use
Land maximum	$(0.6 \times 20) +$	$(1 \times 18) + (1 \times 0)$		$= 30$ acres
Milking shed maximum	$(1 \times 20) +$	$(0 \times 18) + (1 \times 5)$		$= 25$ head
Hay maximum	$(9 \times 20) -$	$(15 \times 18) + (1 \times 270)$		$= 180$ cwt.
Fertility equality	$(0 \times 20) +$	(1×18)		$= 18$ acres
Land minimum	$(0.6 \times 20) +$	$(1 \times 18) - (1 \times 24)$		$= 6$ acres
Fuel minimum	$(14 \times 20) +$	$(2 \times 18) - (1 \times 232)$		$= 84$ gals.

head when there are only 20 cows, as appear in the optimal solution. Thus the value of s_2, the milking-shed maximum constraint slack, is verified in Tableau 5.

The methodology of these checks (applicable to any basis) is stated more formally as follows: Multiply for any constraint the original a coefficient by the levels of each activity, real and slack (or surplus), in the given basis. The sum of these resource uses should just exhaust the original supply, i.e., the original b coefficient. Table 10.5 sets out these calculations for the optimal solution. The reader should check through each one in detail, verifying the values of each coefficient with respect to Figure 10.1. As an exercise he may apply the same set of constraint checks to other tableaux in Table 10.3.[1]

10.4.2 Primal Solution Check

As a check on the values of the basic variables in the optimal tableau (or, again, in any tableau), we may add up the value of total profit accruing to all basic variables to verify that it tallies with total profit as calculated by the computer. This is simply achieved by multiplying the value of each basic variable in the given solution by its net profit coefficient as indicated in the c row of the original tableau. It is easy to see for our problem that at the optimal solution, with 20 head of cows earning \$40 per head and 18 acres of clover earning \$50 per acre, total profit must be $\$(20 \times 40) + (18 \times 50) = \$1,700$, verifying the value output by the computer. For completeness the full calculations are set out in Table 10.6.

Again, as an exercise, the reader may apply this check to previous tableaux.

10.4.3 Dual Solution Check

Remember that the $z - c$-row value for a fully utilized resource in the optimal solution represents the "net product" or "shadow price" of that resource in the equilibrium situation defined at the optimum point. Obviously resources *not* fully utilized (i.e., constraints *not* just exactly met) in the optimal solution must therefore appear in the basis in the form of their slack or surplus variables and hence cannot have a nonzero shadow price in the solution. To illustrate, Figure 10.1 shows that the solution at Q lies in the land maximum constraint and the fertility equality constraint. Hence obtaining more land, for instance, (which would shift the line AB outward to the right) would cause the optimal solution to change, thereby changing total profit. Thus we expect a nonzero shadow price for

---

[1] To illustrate, look at land use in Tableau 3. Here we have x_1 (cows) using $(5.63 \times \frac{3}{5})$ acres $= 3.37$ acres; x_2 (clover) uses up 2.63 acres; and we note that s_1 (slack land) enters the basis at a level of 24 acres. Altogether $3.37 + 2.63 + 24.00 = 30$ acres, the original land supply.

TABLE 10.6

b-column Value of Basic Variable	×	Original c-row Coefficient	=	Total Profit
		$		$
20 head cows	×	40/head	=	800
18 acres clover	×	50/acre	=	900
5 head milking shed max. slack	×	0/acre	=	0
270 cwt. hay max. slack	×	0/cwt.	=	0
24 acres land min. surplus	×	0/acre	=	0
232 gallons fuel min. surplus	×	0/gal.	=	0
TOTAL PROFIT			=	1,700

land to appear (as the $z - c$-row coefficient of variable s_1) in the optimal tableau. On the other hand, hay, for instance, is *not* fully utilized by the combination of variables at Q; hence its slack variable (s_3) must be *basic* in the tableau corresponding to Q and therefore it cannot have a nonzero shadow price: increasing or decreasing the supply of hay (which would shift the line EF up or down) would not affect the optimum at Q.

Tableau 5 of Table 10.3 shows that the shadow price of land is $66.67 per acre. This tells us that any extra land the farmer could obtain would yield a net return of $66.67 per acre, or alternatively, if land supply were cut back, total profit would drop by $66.67 for every acre decrease. The $z - c$ value for the fertility equality artificial has the opposite sign, showing that the above situation is reversed; in other words if the equality requirement for clover were increased, shifting LM to the right, total profit would *fall* by $16.67 for each acre added to the restriction, whereas moving LM to the left, specifying less clover, would increase total profit by $16.67 for each acre decrease.

Finally we see that neither the land minimum nor the fuel minimum constraint influences the final solution; therefore their discarded artificial variables have zero shadow prices in the final $z - c$ row.

In line with the general symmetry of the dual with the primal, it is not surprising that the dual solution to a linear programming problem may be used as a check on the value of total profit for any given tableau, just as the primal solution above was used. Again we shall perform this check on the *optimal* solution to our problem, and the reader may practice by applying the same check to previous matrixes of this example.

We have already seen (in Chapter 7) that at equilibrium total profit is wholly distributed to the factors of production which are effective in producing it; the dollar rate at which each factor is rewarded is measured directly by the imputed shadow prices generated by the dual solution. Thus the *total* reward that can be assigned to any given factor is simply its reward per unit *times* the original number of units of that factor. For example, our optimal solution shows that land is rewarded at a rate of

$66.67 per acre; as there were 30 acres of land in the initial setup of the problem, the total reward to the factor land is calculated as $66.67 × 30 = $2,000. In similar fashion we compute the total "reward" to the only other variable in the optimal solution with a nonzero shadow price, the fertility equality artificial variable. Its imputed price in the final $z - c$ row is $ - 16.67$ per acre, and with an original level of 18 acres for this constraint we obtain a total reward of $ - 16.67 × 18 = $ - 300. Hence the sum of payments to factors is calculated as $2,000 - 300 = $1,700, verifying again the value of the maximand, total profit, in our example.

The full calculation of this dual solution check on the optimal tableau is shown in Table 10.7.

TABLE 10.7

$z - c$-row Value of Nonbasic Variable	×	Original b- Col. Coefficient	=	Total cost
				$
$66.67/acre of slack land	×	30 acres	=	2,000
$0/acre of land minimum artificial	×	6 acres	=	0
$0/gal. of fuel minimum artificial	×	84 gals.	=	0
$ - 16.67/acre of fertility equality artificial	×	18 acres	=	- 300
TOTAL COST			=	1,700

EXERCISES

Solve the following problem. The daily diet for an invalid must contain at least three units of protein and four units of carbohydrate. The only foods the patient may eat are cabbages and milk. A cabbage provides one unit of protein and eight units of carbohydrate; a pint of milk contains six units of protein and 2 of carbohydrate. The desirable ratio of solid to liquid food in the diet dictates that there may be no more than two cabbages for every pint of milk. If a pint of milk and a cabbage each cost 10 cents, what is the unfortunate patient's least-cost ration?

1. Defining x_1 = number of cabbages in the diet

   x_2 = pints of milk in the diet

   s_1 = slack variable for solid/liquid ratio maximum constraint

   s_2, s_3 = surplus variables for protein and carbohydrate minimum restrictions respectively

   s_2, s_3' = artificial variables corresponding to s_2 and s_3 respectively

   write the initial tableau for the simplex solution of this problem.

2. Derive an approximate solution to the problem by graphical means.

3. Suppose the initial tableau for this problem is handed to a computer and the following output is received in due course:

COMPUTER SOLUTION OF MINIMUM-COST DIET PROBLEM

1. Basis Changes

Iteration	Activity In	Activity Out
1	x_1	s_1
2	x_2	s_3'
3	s_1	s_2'

2. Solution Sequence

Primal Solution		Dual Solution		$z' - c'$ Row	
Variable	Value	Variable	Value	Variable	Value

Tableau 1

s_1	0.000	x_1	10.000	x_1	−9.000
s_2'	3.000	x_2	10.000	x_2	−8.000
s_3'	4.000	s_2	0.000	s_2	1.000
		s_3	0.000	s_3	1.000
		Cost	0.000	"Profit"	−7.000

Tableau 2

x_1	0.000	x_2	30.000	x_2	−26.000
s_2'	3.000	s_1	−10.000	s_1	9.000
s_3'	4.000	s_2	0.000	s_2	1.000
		s_3	0.000	s_3	1.000
		Cost	0.000	"Profit"	−7.000

Tableau 3

x_1	0.444	s_1	3.333	s_1	−2.556
x_2	0.222	s_2	0.000	s_2	1.000
s_2'	1.222	s_3	1.667	s_3	−0.445
		Cost	−6.667	"Profit"	−1.222

Tableau 4

x_1	0.391	s_2	1.305	s_2	0.000
x_2	0.435	s_3	1.087	s_3	0.000
s_1	0.478				
		Cost	−8.262	"Profit"	0.000

End of phase I

Optimal solution found

Interpret the solution sequence generated by the computer, and check it out on the graph of this problem from exercise 2.

4. Perform the usual verifications on Tableaux 1 through 4 as generated by the computer, with respect to (a) the constraints, (b) the primal solutions, and (c) the dual solutions.

APPENDIX
Complete Simplex Solution for Chapter 10 Example

Phase I

Tableau 1

	Real Variables		Surplus Variables		Slack Variables			Artificial Variables					
	Cows	Clover	Land	Fuel	Land	Shed	Hay	Fertility	Land	Fuel			
	x_1	x_2	s_5	s_6	s_1	s_2	s_3	s_4'	s_5'	s_6'	b	R	
c row	40	50	0	0	0	0	0	0	0	0	0		
z row	0	0	0	0	0	0	0	0	0	0	0		
$z - c$ row	−40	−50	0	0	0	0	0	0	0	0	0		
													Basic Variables
s_1 Slack land	0.6	1	0	0	1	0	0	0	0	0	30	50	
s_2 Slack shed	1	0	0	0	0	1	0	0	0	0	25	25	
s_3 Slack hay	9	−15	0	0	0	0	1	0	0	0	180	20	
s_4' Artificial (fertility equality)	0	1	0	0	0	0	0	1	0	0	18	—	
s_5' Artificial (land minimum)	0.6	1	−1	0	0	0	0	0	1	0	6	10	
s_6' Artificial (fuel minimum)	14	2	0	−1	0	0	0	0	0	1	84	6	
c' row	0	0	0	0	0	0	0	−1	−1	−1	0		
z' row	−14.6	−4	1	1	0	0	0	−1	−1	−1	−108		
$z' - c'$ row	−14.6	−4	1	1	0	0	0	0	0	0	−108		

Tableau 2

x_1	x_2	s_5	s_6	s_1	s_2	s_3	s_4'	s_5'	s_6'	b	Basic Variables	R
40	50	0	0	0	0	0	0	0	0	0	c row	
40	5.71	0	-2.86	0	0	0	0	0	0	240	z row	
0	-44.29	0	-2.86	0	0	0	0	0	0	240	$z - c$ row	
											Basic Variables	
0	0.91	0	0.04	1	0	0	0	0	0	26.4	s_1 Slack land	29.0
0	-0.14	0	0.07	0	1	0	0	0	0	19	s_2 Slack shed	—
0	-16.29	0	0.64	0	0	1	0	0	0	126	s_3 Slack hay	—
0	1	0	0	0	0	0	1	0	0	18	s_4' Artificial (fertility equality)	18.0
0	0.91	-1	0.04	0	0	0	0	1	0	2.4	s_5 Artificial (land minimum)	2.6
1	0.14	0	-0.07	0	0	0	0	0	0	6	x_1 Cows	42.9
0	0	0	0	0	0	0	-1	-1	-1	0	c' row	
0	-1.91	0	-0.04	0	0	0	-1	-1	-1	-20.4	z' row	
0	-1.91	0	-0.04	0	0	0	0	0	0	-20.4	$z' - c'$ row	

Tableau 3

Basic Variables	x_1	x_2	s_5	s_6	s_1	s_2	s_3	s_4'	s_5'	s_6'	b	R
c row	40	50	0	0	0	0	0	0	0	0	0	
z row	40	50	−48.44	−0.78	0	0	0	0	0	0	356.25	
$z − c$ row	0	0	−48.44	−0.78	0	0	0	0	0	0	356.25	
s_1 Slack land	0	0	1	0	1	0	0	0			24.00	24.00
s_2 Slack shed	0	0	−0.16	0.08	0	1	0	0			19.38	—
s_3 Slack hay	0	0	−17.81	1.41	0	0	1	0			168.75	—
s_4' Artificial (fertility equality)	0	0	1.09	−0.05	0	0	0	1			15.38	14.06
x_2 Clover	0	1	−1.09	0.05	0	0	0	0			2.63	—
x_1 Cows	1	0	0.16	−0.08	0	0	0	0			5.63	35.19
c' row	0	0	0	0	0	0	0	−1	−1	−1	0	
z' row	0	0	−1.09	0.05	0	0	0	−1	−1	−1	−15.38	
$z' − c'$ row	0	0	−1.09	0.05	0	0	0	0	0	0	−15.38	

Tableau 4

	x_1	x_2	s_5	s_6	s_1	s_2	s_3	s_4'	s_5'	s_6'	b	Basic Variables	R
c row	40	50	0	0	0	0	0	0	0	0	0		
z row	40	50	0	−2.86	0	0	0	−44.29	0	0	1037.14		
z − c row	0	0	0	−2.86	0	0	0	−44.29	0	0	1037.14		
	0	0	0	0.04	1	0	0				9.94	s_1 Slack land	248.5
	0	0	0	0.07	0	1	0				21.57	s_2 Slack shed	308.1
	0	0	0	0.64	0	0	1				419.14	s_3 Slack hay	654.9
	0	0	1	−0.04	0	0	0				14.06	s_5 Surplus land	—
	0	1	0	0	0	0	0				18.00	x_2 Clover	—
	1	0	0	−0.07	0	0	0				3.43	x_1 Cows	—
c′ row	0	0	0	0	0	0	0	−1	−1	−1	0		
z′ row	0	0	0	0	0	0	0	−1	−1	−1	0		
z′ − c′ row	0	0	0	0	0	0	0	0	0	0	0		

Phase II

Tableau 5

x_1	x_2	s_5	s_6	s_1	s_2	s_3	s_4'	s_5'	s_6'	b	
40	50	0	0	0	0	0	0	0	0	0	c row
40	50	0	0	66.67	0	0	−16.67	0	0	1700	z row
0	0	0	0	66.67	0	0	−16.67	0	0	1700	z − c row
											Basic Variables
0	0	0	1	23.33	0	0				232	s_6 Surplus fuel
0	0	0	0	−1.67	1	0				5	s_2 Slack shed
0	0	0	0	−15.00	0	1				270	s_3 Slack hay
0	0	1	0	1	0	0				24	s_5 Surplus land
0	1	0	0	0	0	0				18	x_2 Clover
1	0	0	0	1.67	0	0				20	x_1 Cows

COMPUTATIONAL
ASPECTS

PART III

TRANSFORMING SETS
OF SIMULTANEOUS EQUATIONS

11.1 Orientation

In solving linear programming problems in Parts I and II, the emphasis throughout has been on developing an understanding of the logic of the simplex method, rather than on the purely mechanical aspects of this solution procedure. We have become acquainted with the idea of a *basis* as a special solution to any given set of simultaneous constraint equations. We have noted that a tableau containing a basis formed from any given subset of variables can be derived from a tableau containing any other subset by a series of transformations or iterations. One such transformation, as we have seen, introduces into the basis one existing nonbasic variable which reduces to zero an existing basic variable by eliminating it from the basis. Criteria have been outlined by which the basic and the nonbasic variables to be swapped at each iteration can be purposively chosen such that the basis is directed toward an eventual optimum solution.

In Part III we shall consider in full detail the mechanical processes of this solution procedure. To begin with we shall return to the set of simultaneous constraint equations which describes the area of feasible combinations of variables in any given problem. Disregarding temporarily the question of optimization we shall derive a procedure for modifying the numerical coefficients of a set of equations such that the basic solution is moved, through one iteration, from one vertex to an adjacent vertex. Then, returning to the matter of directing the basis toward the *optimum* vertex, we shall reconsider the rules for selection of the variables to be substituted at any iteration. These discussions will lead to the compiling of a set of streamlined rules for the complete solution of simple linear programming problems; the application of these rules will be illustrated in detail with a numerical example. The complications arising when artificial variables are present in the initial basis will then be discussed, and this discussion will lead again to a complete set of rules for the empirical solution of problems in this category. This set of rules will, in turn, be illustrated by a numerical example.

11.2 Operations on Simple Simultaneous Equations

In section 4.1 it was noted that the task in solving general linear programming problems can be expressed initially in terms of finding solutions to sets of simultaneous equations. From elementary algebra we know that simultaneous equations are solved by adding or subtracting pairs of equations after transforming one or more of them in a certain way. This procedure depends on the fact that, first, both sides of an equation may be multiplied or divided by a given number without altering the relation expressed by the equation, and that, second, in a set of simultaneous equations one equation from that set may be added to or subtracted from another equation. The new equation formed in this way will still be consistent with the old ones. For example, suppose we wish to solve this set of simultaneous equations:

$$5p + 2q = 15 \tag{11.1a}$$

$$2p + 3q = 17 \tag{11.1b}$$

In general the standard procedure is to transform one equation such that the coefficient of one of its variables is made equal to that of a corresponding variable in another equation. Addition or subtraction of the two equations will then result in the disappearance of one variable.[1] When there are only two equations with two unknowns, as in (11.1), the value of the other variable can be immediately determined by this procedure. Thus, for example, *dividing* equation (11.1a) by 5 we have

$$p + \tfrac{2}{5}q = 3 \tag{11.1a*}$$

Multiply equation (11.1a*) by 2 to form equation (11.1b′):

$$2p + \tfrac{4}{5}q = 6 \tag{11.1b′}$$

These two operations make the coefficient of p in equation (11.1b′) equal to 2, and therefore equal to that of p in equation (11.1b). Now *subtraction* of equation (11.1b′) from equation (11.1b) yields a new equation without p:

$$0 + 2\tfrac{1}{5}q = 11 \tag{11.1b*}$$

---

[1] In this exposition, a prime (′) is used to indicate an intermediate equation which is a stepping stone to a new equation, and an asterisk, or star (*), is used to denote a desired new equation.

from which, dividing each side by $2\frac{1}{5}$, we obtain $q = 5$. (Substituting 5 for q in either [11.1a] or [11.1b] will then yield $p = 1$.)

Note carefully the sequence of operations in performing the above transformation. It is *divide, multiply, subtract*. We shall see the significance of this sequence later.

11.3 Systems with More Unknowns Than Equations

Since the above example contains as many independent equations as unknowns, an exact numerical solution could be found. But the technique of eliminating variables can be applied equally to systems with more unknowns than equations so that any set of variables can be expressed in terms of any of the others. Let us take as an example a set of equations containing a basis:

$$1p + 0q + 6r = 12 \tag{11.2a}$$

$$0p + 1q + 5r = 15 \tag{11.2b}$$

Here the coefficients of p and q form a 2×2 identity matrix; by setting $r = 0$ we may read values for p and q directly from the right-hand side. In our previous terminology, r is a nonbasic variable and therefore zero, and the values of the basic variables p and q are 12 and 15 respectively.

It is a simple matter to form new equations from (11.2a) and (11.2b) such that p and r are expressed in terms of q, or q and r in terms of p. Furthermore, by controlling the derivation of the new equations we can ensure that they contain a basis formed from the desired subset of variables. Suppose for instance that from (11.2) we wish to derive a new set of equations in which we can find q and r in terms of p. In other words we wish to make q and r basic and p nonbasic. Let the new equations be called (11.2a*) and (11.2b*), corresponding to (11.2a) and (11.2b) respectively. It is apparent that if (11.2a*) and (11.2b*) are to contain a basis formed from q and r, q must retain in (11.2b*) its unity coefficient from (11.2b) and in (11.2a*) its zero coefficient from (11.2a); r, on the other hand, must have a unity coefficient in (11.2a*) and a zero coefficient in (11.2b*). If these conditions are satisfied, the coefficients of q and r in the new equations will form the desired identity matrix.

To transform (11.2a) into (11.2a*) such that q has a coefficient of zero and r a coefficient of unity is simple: divide (11.2a) by the coefficient of r in (11.2a), i.e., by 6. Thus we get

$$\tfrac{1}{6}p + 0q + 1r = 2 \tag{11.2a*}$$

Now we wish to transform (11.2b) such that r disappears, i.e., such that r's coefficient is reduced to zero. Further we want to ensure that in transforming (11.2b) to (11.2b*) the unit coefficient of q remains unchanged. Each of these objectives may be achieved simply by multiplying (11.2a*) by the coefficient of r in (11.2b) and subtracting the resultant equation from (11.2b): r will disappear and the $1q$ in (11.2b), having zero subtracted from it, will remain the same. Thus we have:

Multiply (11.2a*) by 5, i.e., by the coefficient of r in (11.2b), calling this intermediate equation (11.2b′):

$$\tfrac{5}{6}p + 0q + 5r = 10 \tag{11.2b′}$$

Subtract (11.2b′) from (11.2b):

$$-\tfrac{5}{6}p + 1q + 0r = 5 \tag{11.2b*}$$

From the old equations (11.2a) and (11.2b) we have now formed two new equations (11.2a*) and (11.2b*). Let us rename these equations (11.2c) and (11.2d) and write them together:

$$\tfrac{1}{6}p + 0q + 1r = 2 \tag{11.2c}$$

$$-\tfrac{5}{6}p + 1q + 0r = 5 \tag{11.2d}$$

Observe that we have in effect determined q and r in terms of p, for if we let $p = 0$, we get $r = 2$ and $q = 5$ directly from the right-hand side.

Note again the sequence of operations in making this transformation: divide, multiply, subtract. To illustrate further let us use (11.2c) and (11.2d) to derive another set of equations (11.2c*) and (11.2d*), this time to give p and r in terms of q.

First form (11.2d*) by dividing (11.2d) by $-\tfrac{5}{6}$ to bring p's coefficient to unity:

$$1p - \tfrac{6}{5}q + 0r = -6 \tag{11.2d*}$$

Now form an intermediate equation from (11.2d*) by multiplying (11.2d*) by $\tfrac{1}{6}$ to make its p coefficient equal to that of p in (11.2c), calling the intermediate equation (11.2c′):

$$\tfrac{1}{6}p - \tfrac{1}{5}q + 0r = -1 \tag{11.2c′}$$

Subtract (11.2c′) from (11.2c) in order to eliminate p:

$$0p + \tfrac{1}{5}q + 1r = 3 \tag{11.2c*}$$

Rewrite (11.2c*) and (11.2d*) together, renaming then (11.2e) and (11.2f):

$$0p + \tfrac{1}{5}q + 1r = 3 \tag{11.2e}$$

$$1p - \tfrac{6}{5}q + 0r = -6 \tag{11.2f}$$

We now have in effect determined p and r in terms of q; by letting $q = 0$, a direct reading of $r = 3$ and $p = -6$ is given from the right-hand side.

From (11.2e) and (11.2f) a new set of equations (11.2e*) and (11.2f*) could be formed to express p and q in terms of r. This would bring the calculation around full circle, since the original equations (11.2a) and (11.2b) would reappear.[2]

11.4 A Larger Problem

We shall now apply these techniques to a larger problem, which has a similar structure to the one solved in section 11.3. Let us take, in fact, the set of constraints corresponding to the simple maximization example from Chapter 1, which consists of three equations:

$$1x_1 + 2x_2 + 1s_1 + 0s_2 + 0s_3 = \ 8 \tag{11.3a}$$

$$3x_1 + 1x_2 + 0s_1 + 1s_2 + 0s_3 = 12 \tag{11.3b}$$

$$1x_1 + 1x_2 + 0s_1 + 0s_2 + 1s_3 = \ 5 \tag{11.3c}$$

Remember that as the equations are set up here we can solve for s_1, s_2, and s_3 in terms of x_1 and x_2; in other words, with x_1 and x_2 nonbasic, i.e., zero, we arrive at direct solutions for the basic variables s_1, s_2, and s_3; viz., $s_1 = 8$, $s_2 = 12$, $s_3 = 5$. Now, using the above techniques, let us form a new set of equations (11.3a*), (11.3b*), and (11.3c*), which will express, say, s_2, s_3, and x_2 in terms of the remaining variables x_1 and s_1. Following the notation used in connection with equations (4.5) and (4.6) we can express this problem as one of determining the unknown coefficients marked by question marks in the following system:

$$?x_1 + 1x_2 + ?s_1 \qquad\qquad = \ ? \tag{11.3a*}$$

$$?x_1 \qquad + ?s_1 + 1s_2 \qquad = \ ? \tag{11.3b*}$$

$$?x_1 \qquad + ?s_1 \qquad + 1s_3 = \ ? \tag{11.3c*}$$

By setting x_1 and x_2 equal to zero we can then read off the values of x_2, s_2, and s_3 down the right-hand column.

---

[2] The calculations are as follows:

1. Divide (11.2e) by $\frac{1}{5}$ to give (11.2e*):
$$0p + 1q + 5r = 15 \tag{11.2e*}$$

2. Multiply (11.2e*) by $-\frac{6}{5}$ to give (11.2f'):
$$0p - \tfrac{6}{5}q - 6r = -18 \tag{11.2f'}$$

3. Subtract (11.2f') from (11.2f) to give (11.2f*):
$$1p + 0q + 6r = 12 \tag{11.2f*}$$

Rename (11.2f*) as (11.2a) and (11.2e*) as (11.2b):
$$1p + 0q + 6r = 12 \tag{11.2a}$$
$$0p + 1q + 5r = 15 \tag{11.2b}$$

The procedure of transformation is exactly as before. Since we wish to form a basis from the variables x_2, s_2, and s_3, we must ensure:

1. That the coefficient of x_2 in (11.3a) is transformed to unity in (11.3a*) and that the coefficients of x_2 in (11.3b) and (11.3c) are reduced to zero in (11.3b*) and (11.3c*).
2. That s_2 retains in (11.3b*) its unity coefficient from (11.3b), and in (11.3a*) and (11.3c*) its zero coefficients from (11.3a) and (11.3c).
3. That s_3 retains in (11.3c*) its unity coefficient from (11.3c), and in (11.3a*) and (11.3b*) its zero coefficients from (11.3a) and (11.3b).

Attending to (1) first, form (11.3a*) by dividing (11.3a) by the coefficient of x_2 in (11.3a):

$$\tfrac{1}{2}x_1 + 1x_2 + \tfrac{1}{2}s_1 + 0s_2 + 0s_3 = 4 \qquad (11.3a^*)$$

Now each of the remaining equations, i.e., (11.3b) and (11.3c), must be transformed to conform to the requirements in (2) and (3) above. As before, intermediate equations will be formed from (11.3a*) for both (11.3b) and (11.3c), called (11.3b′) and (11.3c′). These will be multiples of (11.3a*) such that in (11.3b′) the coefficient of x_2 will be the same as that in (11.3b), and in (11.3c′) the coefficient of x_2 will be the same as that in (11.3c). Then when (11.3b′) is subtracted from (11.3b) to give (11.3b*), x_2 will disappear. Likewise (11.3c′) will be subtracted from (11.3c) to give (11.3c*), again causing x_2 to disappear.

Thus, the individual steps are as follows: From (11.3a*) form the intermediate equation (11.3b′) by multiplying (11.3a*) by the coefficient of x_2 in (11.3b), i.e., by 1:

$$\tfrac{1}{2}x_1 + 1x_2 + \tfrac{1}{2}s_1 + 0s_2 + 0s_3 = 4 \qquad (11.3b′)$$

Subtract (11.3b′) from (11.3b) to give the new equation (11.3b*) from which x_2 has now disappeared:

$$2\tfrac{1}{2}x_1 + 0x_2 - \tfrac{1}{2}s_1 + 1s_2 + 0s_3 = 8 \qquad (11.3b^*)$$

Repeating for (11.3c), from (11.3a*) form the intermediate equation (11.3c′) by multiplying (11.3a*) by the coefficient of x_2 in (11.3c), i.e., by 1:

$$\tfrac{1}{2}x_1 + 1x_2 + \tfrac{1}{2}s_1 + 0s_2 + 0s_3 = 4 \qquad (11.3c′)$$

Subtract (11.3c′) from (11.3c) to give the new equation (11.3c*) from which x_2 has now also disappeared:

$$\tfrac{1}{2}x_1 + 0x_2 - \tfrac{1}{2}s_1 + 0s_2 + 1s_3 = 1 \qquad (11.3c^*)$$

Rewrite the new set of equations (11.3a*), (11.3b*), and (11.3c*) in order, renaming them (11.3e), (11.3f), and (11.3g).:

$$\tfrac{1}{2}x_1 + 1x_2 + \tfrac{1}{2}s_1 + 0s_2 + 0s_3 = 4 \tag{11.3e}$$

$$2\tfrac{1}{2}x_1 + 0x_2 - \tfrac{1}{2}s_1 + 1s_2 + 0s_3 = 8 \tag{11.3f}$$

$$\tfrac{1}{2}x_1 + 0x_2 - \tfrac{1}{2}s_1 + 0s_2 + 1s_3 = 1 \tag{11.3g}$$

Observe that we have now fulfilled requirements (1), (2), and (3) above, having determined x_2, s_2, and s_3 in terms of x_1 and s_1. Thus, with the non-basic variables x_1 and s_1 both zero, the values of the basic variables are given directly from the right-hand side as $x_2 = 4$, $s_2 = 8$, $s_3 = 1$.

Notice again the sequence of operations in carrying out this transformation. First one equation is *divided* throughout by the coefficient of the variable which is to be made basic. Then, on *each* one of the remaining equations, operations of *multiplication* and *subtraction* are performed so as to reduce to zero the coefficient of that chosen variable in each equation.

11.5 Tableau Presentation of These Basic Solutions

The results of each of the above set of operations may be set up by using the more elegant tableau presentation with which we have become familiar. Looking first at the successive transformations performed on the simultaneous equations from (11.2), we can write each new set of equations as a separate tableau (omitting the intermediate equations) as in Table 11.1. We write the name of each basic variable beside its b-column coefficient.

Similarly for the constraints of the maximization example from equation (11.3) the original and the new set of equations can be written in detached coefficient form as in Table 11.2.

We have noted that a basis can only depict a combination of variables lying at a *vertex* of the constraint set. Refer to any diagram of the constraint set for the maximization example, say Figure 9.1. Which vertex in this figure is represented by Tableau 2 of Table 11.2? Clearly the combination $x_1 = 0$, $x_2 = 4$, $s_1 = 0$, $s_2 = 8$, $s_3 = 1$ represents point B in Figure 9.1. At this point no wheat is produced, 4 bushels of barley are produced, labor is slack by 8 man-hours, fertilizer is slack by 1 hundred-weight, and there is no slack land.

It is apparent, then, that by transforming Tableau 1 into Tableau 2 in Table 11.2 we have "moved" the basis from the origin O in Figure 9.1 to the adjacent vertex B. This movement comprises *one* iteration. In the next chapter we shall demonstrate how the basis may be moved to other vertexes of the feasible region. Indeed we shall move it right around the region and back to the origin. Further, we shall show how tableaux may be

TABLE 11.1

Tableau 1

p	q	r	b	
				Basic Variables
1	0	6	12	p
0	1	5	15	q

Tableau 2

p	q	r	b	
				Basic Variables
$\frac{1}{6}$	0	1	2	r
$-\frac{5}{6}$	1	0	5	q

Tableau 3

p	q	r	b	
				Basic Variables
0	$\frac{1}{5}$	1	3	r
1	$-\frac{6}{5}$	0	-6	p

TABLE 11.2

Tableau 1

x_1	x_2	s_1	s_2	s_3	b	
						Basic Variables
1	2	1	0	0	8	s_1
3	1	0	1	0	12	s_2
1	1	0	0	1	5	s_3

Tableau 2

x_1	x_2	s_1	s_2	s_3	b	
						Basic Variables
$\frac{1}{2}$	1	$\frac{1}{2}$	0	0	4	x_2
$2\frac{1}{2}$	0	$-\frac{1}{2}$	1	0	8	s_2
$\frac{1}{2}$	0	$-\frac{1}{2}$	0	1	1	s_3

transformed (i.e., the coefficients of new sets of equations determined) by means of streamlined rules of thumb; in particular we will be able to by-pass the explicit writing-down of the intermediate equations in the above procedure, by combining two of the steps into one.

EXERCISES

1. Solve for the unknowns in the following sets of simultaneous equations:

   a. $2x + 3y = 16$
      $3x - 5y = 5$

   b. $3x - 2y + 8z = 13$
      $2x + 5y - 3z = 13$
      $7x - 3y - 5z = 10$

2. From the following set of equations:

   $1x + \tfrac{1}{2}y + 0z = 6$
   $0x + 3y + 1z = 2$

   determine the unknown coefficients in the following:

   a. $?x + 1y + 0z = \,?$
      $?x + 0y + 1z = \,?$

   and

   b. $1x + 0y + ?z = \,?$
      $0x + 1y + ?z = \,?$

   Use the notation developed in this chapter for naming the equations (viz., [a], [a'], [a*], and so on).
3. Show how the coefficients of the equations in part (a) of exercise 2 may be derived directly from the equations in part (b).
4. Classify basic and nonbasic variables in the three sets of equations in exercise 2, and write the values of all variables under these assumptions in each case.
5. The following set of equations contains a basis made up of x_2, s_2, and s_3:

$$\tfrac{1}{2}x_1 + 1x_2 + \tfrac{1}{2}s_1 + 0s_2 + 0s_3 = 4 \tag{a}$$

$$2\tfrac{1}{2}x_1 + 0x_2 - \tfrac{1}{2}s_1 + 1s_2 + 0s_3 = 8 \tag{b}$$

$$\tfrac{1}{2}x_1 + 0x_2 - \tfrac{1}{2}s_1 + 0s_2 + 1s_3 = 1 \tag{c}$$

Form a new set of equations (a*), (b*), and (c*) containing a basis made up of s_1, s_2, and s_3. Set out all details of your calculations, using the methods employed in this chapter.

6. Use equations (a), (b), and (c) from exercise 5 to form a new set of equations (a*), (b*), and (c*) containing a basis made up of the variables x_1, x_2, and s_2.
7. Present in tableau form your answers to exercises 5 and 6.

SUCCESSIVE CHANGES
OF THE BASIS

12.1 Swapping Variables

In Chapter 11 we saw how the original basis for our maximization problem (Tableau 1 in Table 11.2) could be transformed into a new basis (Tableau 2). This transformation constitutes one iteration of the simplex procedure; as seen in section 5.2 *one* iteration introduces *one* currently nonbasic variable into the basis, eliminating *one* currently basic variable. Thus, as already noted, a single iteration can move the solution from its current vertex of the constraint set to an adjacent one.

We now wish to demonstrate a *series* of basis changes. Still using the simple wheat/barley example, we shall illustrate by tracing a path around the whole of the feasible region. If we choose to move in a counter-clockwise direction, five iterations, numbered 1 to 5 in Figure 12.1, will be involved.

First we must list which variable is to replace which other variable in the basis at each step in order to move the solution to the next desired vertex. Table 5.1 lists which variables are basic and which nonbasic at each vertex of the constraint set in our example. Table 12.1 indicates which

TABLE 12.1

Iteration	Movement of Solution on Figure 12.1	Variable to Be Introduced into the Basis	Variable to Be Eliminated from the Basis
1	O to B	x_2	s_1
2	B to H	x_1	s_3
3	H to E	s_1	s_2
4	E to C	s_3	x_2
5	C to O	s_2	x_1

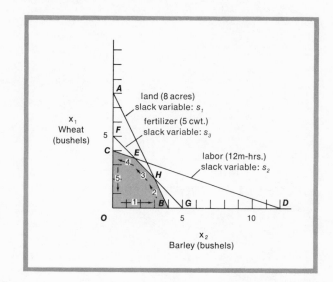

Figure 12.1

variable should be introduced and which eliminated at each iteration in order to move the basis through the path shown on Figure 12.1. The reader should check back to Table 5.1 to verify this list of variables to be swapped at each step. Remember that for the moment we are not concerned with optimization, so the rules derived in section 5.4 for the choice of variables to be substituted are not applicable here; we shall be returning to these rules in the next chapter.

12.2   First Iteration

The procedure for transforming sets of simultaneous equations derived in the preceding chapter will now be streamlined into a set of five "rules" which are applicable to any tableau. Let us call any tableau to be modified

TABLE 12.2

Tableau 1 (corresponding to vertex O in Figure 12.1)

(1)	(2)	(3)	(4)	(5)	(6)	
x_1	x_2	s_1	s_2	s_3	b	
						Basic Variables
1	②	1	0	0	8	s_1 ←
3	1	0	1	0	12	s_2
1	1	0	0	1	5	s_3

the *old tableau* and the tableau which results after transformation the *new tableau*. In this section we shall illustrate the application of these rules to the transformation of our initial tableau in accordance with iteration 1 in Table 12.1. Thus, with respect to iteration 1, the tableau containing the initial basis will be the old tableau, and that containing the basis at point *B* will be the new tableau. The initial tableau is shown in Table 12.2.

The reader will, of course, have noted that we have already calculated iteration 1, deriving it from first principles in Chapter 11. Thus we shall have an opportunity for comparing the streamlined set of rules listed below with the logic of the calculation procedure in the previous chapter.

Rule 1

Decide on the variable to be introduced into the basis. Call this the *introduced variable*. We read from Table 12.1 that for the first iteration in our example the introduced variable is to be x_2. Mark its *column* in the old tableau by a vertical arrow ($\uparrow$), as shown in Table 12.2.

Rule 2

Decide on the variable to be eliminated from the basis. Call this the *eliminated variable*. Again, we read from Table 12.1 that for the first iteration, s_1 is to be the eliminated variable. Mark its *row* in the old tableau by a horizontal arrow ($\leftarrow$), as shown in Table 12.2.

Rule 3

In the old tableau, locate the coefficient at the intersection of the introduced variable column and the eliminated variable row. Call this coefficient the *pivot*. In Tableau 1 of our example the pivot coefficient is at the intersection of the x_2 column and the s_1 row; its value is 2. Encircle it as shown in Table 12.2.

Rule 4

We now come to the beginning of the actual computations. The first task is equivalent to that embodied in the calculation of equation (11.3a*) in section 11.4, i.e., the formation of a new equation in which the coefficient of the new basic variable is unity. In tableau form we shall identify the row in the new tableau corresponding to the newly introduced basic variable as the *incoming row*. The elements of the incoming row are calculated by dividing each coefficient in the eliminated variable row in the old tableau by the pivot. Thus to form the incoming row for Tableau 2 in our example, each coefficient in the s_1 row of Tableau 1 (Table 12.2) must be divided by 2. Working from left to right across the line we have:

$$1 \div 2 = \tfrac{1}{2}$$
$$2 \div 2 = 1$$
$$1 \div 2 = \tfrac{1}{2}$$
$$0 \div 2 = 0$$
$$0 \div 2 = 0$$
$$8 \div 2 = 4$$

The incoming row should be written in the new tableau in the same position as the eliminated variable row in the old tableau. In our example the eliminated variable occupied the *first* row in the old tableau; hence the incoming row is written as the *first* row in the new tableau. At this point in the calculation, then, the new tableau 2 appears as in Table 12.3. Note, also, that in the Basic Variables column at the extreme right of Table 12.3, we have entered x_2 in place of s_1.

TABLE 12.3

Tableau 2

(1)	(2)	(3)	(4)	(5)	(6)	
x_1	x_2	s_1	s_2	s_3	b	
						Basic Variables
$\tfrac{1}{2}$	1	$\tfrac{1}{2}$	0	0	4	x_2
						s_2
						s_3

Rule 5

We now wish to transform the remainder of the old tableau, i.e., calculate the coefficients of equations (11.3b*) and (11.3c*) in section 11.4. An opportunity for streamlining the procedure of the previous chapter arises here, enabling us to by-pass the explicit writing-down of the intermediate equations (11.3b') and (11.3c') of section 11.4. We can state a general rule which may be applied to *any* remaining coefficient in the old tableau in order to calculate directly the value of the corresponding coefficient in the new tableau.

First, write the coefficients of the *outgoing* column of the old tableau.

For our example the outgoing column at iteration 1 is that of x_2 in Table 12.2, written as follows:

Row Number (i) in Tableau

2	1
1	2
1	3

Second, write the coefficients of the *newly formed* incoming row of the new tableau. For iteration 1 this is as follows:

$\frac{1}{2}$	1	$\frac{1}{2}$	0	0	4
1	2	3	4	5	6

Column Number (j) in Tableau

Now, the rule is stated as follows. From the coefficient at the intersection of the ith row and the jth column of the *old* tableau must be subtracted the product of the ith-row coefficient in the outgoing column and the jth-column coefficient in the incoming row. This will give a new coefficient, which will be written at the intersection of the ith row and the jth column of the new tableau.

To illustrate, the coefficient at the intersection of the second row and the first column in old Tableau 1 in Table 12.2 is 3. The corresponding coefficient in Tableau 2 is therefore calculated as 3 *minus* the product of (second-row coefficient in the outgoing column [$= 1$] and the first-column coefficient in the incoming row [$= \frac{1}{2}$]) or $3 - (1 \times \frac{1}{2}) = 2\frac{1}{2}$. This will be entered in Tableau 2 at the intersection of the second row and the first column. Similarly, the third-row sixth-column coefficient in Tableau 1 is 5. The corresponding element in the new tableau will be 5 *minus* the product of (third-row coefficient in the outgoing column [$= 1$] and sixth-column coefficient in the incoming row [$= 4$]) or $5 - (1 \times 4) = 1$.

The full calculations are set out in Table 12.4, working across each row from left to right. This calculation procedure generates the coefficients of equations (11.3b*) and (11.3c*) in section 11.4. Observe in particular the way in which the coefficients of x_2 in the second and third rows of the tableau are reduced to zero such that the new x_2 column, already containing a single unity coefficient (as the element in the incoming row), now also contains zeros in all other rows.[1] Thus the x_2 column in new Tableau 2 forms part of the new identity matrix. Notice also the way in which the

---

[1] The reader may prove for himself that the remaining coefficients in the outgoing column *must* be reduced to zero in the new tableau by this transformation process.

TABLE 12.4

	Coefficient in Tableau 1	−	Outgoing Column Element	×	Incoming Row Element	=	Coefficient in Tableau 2

First Row
Incoming row: Already calculated

Second Row

Col. 1	3	−	(1	×	$\frac{1}{2}$)	=	$2\frac{1}{2}$
2	1	−	(1	×	1)	=	0
3	0	−	(1	×	$\frac{1}{2}$)	=	$-\frac{1}{2}$
4	1	−	(1	×	0)	=	1
5	0	−	(1	×	0)	=	0
6	12	−	(1	×	4)	=	8

Third Row

Col. 1	1	−	(1	×	$\frac{1}{2}$)	=	$\frac{1}{2}$
2	1	−	(1	×	1)	=	0
3	0	−	(1	×	$\frac{1}{2}$)	=	$-\frac{1}{2}$
4	0	−	(1	×	0)	=	0
5	1	−	(1	×	0)	=	1
6	5	−	(1	×	4)	=	1

remaining columns of the identity matrix (corresponding to the currently basic variables s_2 and s_3) remain unchanged in the new tableau.

The completed Tableau 2 is shown in Table 12.5. Setting the nonbasic variables x_1 and s_1 to zero, we read the solution $x_2 = 4, s_2 = 8, s_3 = 1$ from

TABLE 12.5

Tableau 2

(1)	(2)	(3)	(4)	(5)	(6)	
x_1	x_2	s_1	s_2	s_3	b	
						Basic Variables
$\frac{1}{2}$	1	$\frac{1}{2}$	0	0	4	x_2
$2\frac{1}{2}$	0	$-\frac{1}{2}$	1	0	8	s_2
$\frac{1}{2}$	0	$-\frac{1}{2}$	0	1	1	s_3←

Tableau 2. As we know, this combination of variables corresponds to point *B* in Figure 12.1.

12.3 Second Iteration

Let us illustrate again the operation of the above five rules by applying them to Tableau 2 in order to shift the solution through the next iteration. According to our predetermined plan shown in Table 12.1, iteration 2 will move the basis from B to H in Figure 12.1.

Rule 1

Table 12.1 shows that the introduced variable at this iteration is to be x_1. Mark its column in Tableau 2 by a vertical arrow, as shown in Table 12.5.

Rule 2

Table 12.1 shows that the eliminated variable at this iteration is to be s_3. Mark its row in the old tableau by a horizontal arrow, as shown in Table 12.5.

Rule 3

Encircle the pivot, which is the coefficient $\frac{1}{2}$, at the intersection of column x_1 and row s_3 in Tableau 2, Table 12.5.

Rule 4

Form the incoming row by dividing each element in the s_3 row of Tableau 2 by the pivot. Working from left to right we have

$$
\begin{aligned}
\tfrac{1}{2} \div \tfrac{1}{2} &= 1 \\
0 \div \tfrac{1}{2} &= 0 \\
-\tfrac{1}{2} \div \tfrac{1}{2} &= -1 \\
0 \div \tfrac{1}{2} &= 0 \\
1 \div \tfrac{1}{2} &= 2 \\
1 \div \tfrac{1}{2} &= 2
\end{aligned}
$$

Since the row of the eliminated variable in the old tableau was the third row (the s_3 row) in that tableau, the newly calculated incoming row will of course also be written into Tableau 3 as the third row.

Rule 5

Identify the outgoing column in the old tableau and write it separately as below. It is the x_1 column of Tableau 2, Table 12.5:

Row Number in Tableau

$\frac{1}{2}$	1
$2\frac{1}{2}$	2
$\frac{1}{2}$	3

Next identify the incoming row of new tableau 3. It is the row calculated by the application of rule 4:

1	0	−1	0	2	2

Column Number   1   2   3   4   5   6
in Tableau

Now modify the remaining coefficients of Tableau 2. From the ith-row j^{th}-column coefficient of Tableau 2 subtract the product of the ith-row coefficient in the outgoing column and j^{th}-column coefficient in the incoming row. The calculations are shown in full in Table 12.6.

TABLE 12.6

	Coefficient in Tableau 2	−	Outgoing Column Element	×	Incoming Row Element	=	Coefficient in Tableau 3
First Row							
Col. 1	$\frac{1}{2}$	−	($\frac{1}{2}$	×	1)	=	0
2	1	−	($\frac{1}{2}$	×	0)	=	1
3	$\frac{1}{2}$	−	($\frac{1}{2}$	×	−1)	=	1
4	0	−	($\frac{1}{2}$	×	0)	=	0
5	0	−	($\frac{1}{2}$	×	2)	=	−1
6	4	−	($\frac{1}{2}$	×	2)	=	3
Second Row							
Col. 1	$2\frac{1}{2}$	−	($2\frac{1}{2}$	×	1)	=	0
2	0	−	($2\frac{1}{2}$	×	0)	=	0
3	$-\frac{1}{2}$	−	($2\frac{1}{2}$	×	−1)	=	2
4	1	−	($2\frac{1}{2}$	×	0)	=	1
5	0	−	($2\frac{1}{2}$	×	2)	=	−5
6	8	−	($2\frac{1}{2}$	×	2)	=	3

Third Row
Incoming row: Already calculated

TABLE 12.7

Tableau 3

1	2	3	4	5	6	
x_1	x_2	s_1	s_2	s_3	b	
						Basic Variables
0	1	1	0	−1	3	x_2
0	0	2	1	−5	3	s_2
1	0	−1	0	2	2	x_1

The complete new Tableau 3 is written as shown in Table 12.7. Note that x_1 has replaced s_3 in the Basic Variables identification column at the right-hand side of the tableau. Setting the new nonbasic variables, s_1 and s_3, equal to zero, we can read off the solution $x_2 = 3$, $s_2 = 3$, and $x_1 = 2$. It is a simple matter to verify that a combination of $x_1 = 2$, $x_2 = 3$, $s_1 = 0$, $s_2 = 3$, $s_3 = 0$ corresponds to point H on Figure 12.1.

12.4 The Remaining Iterations

By a further application of the above five rules, Tableau 3 may be transformed through iteration 3 into Tableau 4, shifting the basis to point E on Figure 12.1. Then iterations 4 and 5 may be performed, yielding Tableaux 5 and 6 by two further applications of the rules. This moves the solution through point C back to point O, the origin. It is left for the reader to carry out the detailed calculations, using the above techniques. Table 12.8 summarizes the results over all five iterations. In this table, tableaux 1 through 6 are shown, corresponding to the sequence of points O, B, H, E, C, and O in Figure 12.1. It will be seen that in Tableau 6 the order

TABLE 12.8

Tableau 1

x_1	x_2	s_1	s_2	s_3	b	
						Basic Variables
1	②	1	0	0	8	s_1 Slack land ←
3	1	0	1	0	12	s_2 Slack labor
1	1	0	0	1	5	s_3 Slack fertilizer

Iteration 1

Tableau 2

x_1	x_2	s_1	s_2	s_3	b	
						Basic Variables
½	1	½	0	0	4	x_2 Barley
2½	0	−½	1	0	8	s_2 Slack labor
½	0	−½	0	1	1	s_3 Slack fertilizer ←

Iteration 2

Tableau 3

x_1	x_2	s_1	s_2	s_3	b	
						Basic Variables
0	1	1	0	-1	3	x_2 Barley
0	0	②	1	-5	3	s_2 Slack labor $\leftarrow$
1	0	-1	0	2	2	x_1 Wheat

$\uparrow$

Iteration 3

Tableau 4

x_1	x_2	s_1	s_2	s_3	b	
						Basic Variables
0	1	0	$-\frac{1}{2}$	$1\frac{1}{2}$	$1\frac{1}{2}$	x_2 Barley $\leftarrow$
0	0	1	$\frac{1}{2}$	$-2\frac{1}{2}$	$1\frac{1}{2}$	s_1 Slack land
1	0	0	$\frac{1}{2}$	$-\frac{1}{2}$	$3\frac{1}{2}$	x_1 Wheat

$\uparrow$

Iteration 4

Tableau 5

x_1	x_2	s_1	s_2	s_3	b	
						Basic Variables
0	$\frac{2}{3}$	0	$-\frac{1}{3}$	1	1	s_3 Slack fertilizer
0	$1\frac{2}{3}$	1	$-\frac{1}{3}$	0	4	s_1 Slack land
1	$\frac{1}{3}$	0	$\frac{1}{3}$	0	4	x_1 Wheat $\leftarrow$

$\uparrow$

Iteration 5

Tableau 6

x_1	x_2	s_1	s_2	s_3	b	
						Basic Variables
1	1	0	0	1	5	s_3 Slack fertilizer
1	2	1	0	0	8	s_1 Slack land
3	1	0	1	0	12	s_2 Slack labor

Tableau 6A

x_1	x_2	s_1	s_2	s_3	b	
						Basic Variables
1	2	1	0	0	8	s_1 Slack land
3	1	0	1	0	12	s_2 Slack labor
1	1	0	0	1	5	s_3 Slack fertilizer

of the rows turns out to be different from that of Tableau 1, although numerically the two matrixes are identical. Thus, by rewriting Tableau 6 with its first row at the bottom, Tableau 6A is obtained, which is identical with Tableau 1 in all respects.

As we have seen, each tableau in Table 12.8 represents the coefficients of a set of simultaneous equations. The variables in each set may be divided into basic and nonbasic variables, such that by setting nonbasic variables to zero, the values of the basic variables may be read from the b column of the tableau. Table 12.9 lists the solution contained in each tableau of Table 12.8.

TABLE 12.9

Tableau	Value of Variable					Point on Figure 12.1
	x_1	x_2	s_1	s_2	s_3	
1	0	0	8	12	5	O
2	0	4	0	8	1	B
3	2	3	0	3	0	H
4	$3\frac{1}{2}$	$1\frac{1}{2}$	$1\frac{1}{2}$	0	0	E
5	4	0	4	0	1	C
6, 6A	0	0	8	12	5	O

This chapter has shown how a step-by-step process may generate a series of solutions to our problem. In the following chapters, we shall re-examine the principles that enable us to choose introduced and eliminated variables at any iteration such that the solution moves toward an optimum.

EXERCISES

1. For Tableau 1 of Table 11.1, apply the five rules derived in this chapter to introduce the variable r, replacing variable p, in the basis in this tableau. Compare this procedure with the algebraic derivation of Tableau 2 from Tableau 1 given in section 11.3. Next use the set of five rules to calculate Tableau 3 from Tableau 2 of Table 11.1.

2. Given the following tableau:

x_1	x_2	x_3	s_1	s_2	s_3	b	
							Basic Variables
$\frac{1}{4}$	0	2	1	$\frac{1}{2}$	0	6	s_1
$-\frac{1}{4}$	1	8	0	$-\frac{1}{2}$	0	3	x_2
-1	0	1	0	$\frac{1}{2}$	1	9	s_3

calculate the coefficients of new tableaux containing bases formed from

a. x_1, x_2, s_3
b. x_3, s_1, s_3
c. x_2, s_2, s_3

3. Introduce x_1 into the following degenerate basis, replacing s_1:

x_1	x_2	s_1	s_2	b	
					Basic Variables
3	-2	1	0	0	s_1
1	1	0	1	5	s_2

Check your answer with Table 9.4.

4. Refer to the example from the exercises in Chapter 4. List the sequences of variables which could be swapped to form, from the initial basis, the bases specified in parts (a), (b), and (c) of exercise 3 in Chapter 4. (You need list only one sequence for each part of this exercise.)

5. Applying the five rules presented in this chapter, perform the calculations for the sequence of iterations for each part of exercise 4 above.

6. Verify graphically the values of the basic variables from the previous exercise.

13

TOWARD THE OPTIMUM

13.1 Choice Rules for Variables to Be Substituted

In Chapter 12 the technique of transforming a basis was illustrated without regard to the process of optimization. Five rules were listed whose application would yield one iteration of the simplex. Of these rules the first two dealt with the choice of variables to be substituted. In the illustration in Chapter 12 we had decided *beforehand* which variables to swap at each iteration, since we had a predetermined path to follow (i.e., counter-clockwise right around the diagram of the constraint set). Thus rules 1 and 2 as defined in that chapter simply referred us to a prearranged sequence of variables to be swapped, as was set out in Table 12.1.

In Chapter 5, however, in discussing the basic ideas of the simplex, we derived rules that may be applied to determine which activity should enter the basis and which should leave at any iteration in order that the solution may be directed toward the optimum vertex. Moreover, incorporated in these rules are the means by which the optimum solution can be recognized when it is finally reached.

To formulate a complete set of rules for finding the optimum solution to any problem of maximization subject to maximum constraints, it will now be necessary only to substitute these two explicit selection procedures for rules 1 and 2 as stated in Chapter 12.

Let us write rules 1 and 2 in full. Their mechanics have already been illustrated in section 5.4.1 (rule 1) and section 5.4.2 (rule 2), and the reader should recheck these sections carefully before proceeding. In section 13.2 we finalize the illustration of the rules by applying them to the complete solution of our simple maximization problem.

Rule 1. Selection of Activity to Enter the Basis

Rule 1A.   Write down the c row.

Rule 1B.   Calculate the z row.

Rule 1C.   Calculate the $z - c$ row.

Rule 1D.   Examine all coefficients in the $z - c$ row.

a. If all are either *zero* or *positive*, no activity that will increase profit can be introduced into the basis. The basis contained in this tableau is therefore optimal, and the required solution has been reached.

b. If the $z - c$-row coefficients of one or more nonbasic variables are *negative*, select as the activity to enter the basis the one with the *largest negative* $z - c$-*row coefficient.*

Rule 2. Selection of Activity to Leave the Basis

Rule 2A.   Calculate the R column.

Rule 2B.   Examine all coefficients in the R column. Select as the activity to leave the basis the one with the *smallest* R *value.*

13.2   Application of the Optimization Choice Rules to the Maximization Example

In this section we illustrate rules 1A to 1D and 2A and 2B by applying them to our maximization example. Chapter 12 has already given full details of the transformation procedure for the main tableau (i.e., rules 3 to 5); thus here we need only demonstrate the choice of the introduced and the eliminated variables at each iteration.

Table 13.1 sets out the full solution procedure, starting with the initial tableau and working through to the optimal basis. The notes given below should assist in following through the steps of the solution.

Iteration 1

Rule 1A.   The c coefficients are taken directly from the equation to be maximized. Positive coefficients represent profits, and negative coefficients represent costs, per unit of activity. Thus, for instance, the coefficient 4 for x_1 indicates that 1 bushel of wheat returns a profit of \$4.

Rule 1B.   The coefficients of the z row indicate, for a given activity in the tableau, the profit opportunities forgone as a result of introducing one unit of that activity into the basis. These opportunity costs arise because when one variable replaces another in the basis, the levels of all existing basic variables may change. The calculation of the z-row coefficients was outlined in section 5.3.

In Tableau 1 of Table 13.1, the existing basic variables are all slack activities with zero c-row coefficients. Thus any change in their values

TABLE 13.1

Tableau 1

Real Variables		Slack Variables				
Wheat	Barley	Land	Labor	Ferti-lizer		
x_1	x_2	s_1	s_2	s_3	b	
4	6	0	0	0	0	c row
0	0	0	0	0	0	z row R
−4	−6	0	0	0	0	$z - c$ row
						Basic Variables
1	②	1	0	0	8	s_1 Slack land 4←
3	1	0	1	0	12	s_2 Slack labor 12
1	1	0	0	1	5	s_3 Slack fertilizer 5

↑

Tableau 2

x_1	x_2	s_1	s_2	s_3	b	
4	6	0	0	0	0	c row
3	6	3	0	0	24	z row R
−1	0	3	0	0	24	$z - c$ row
						Basic Variables
½	1	½	0	0	4	x_2 Barley 8
2½	0	−½	1	0	8	s_2 Slack labor 3⅕
①½	0	−½	0	1	1	s_3 Slack fertilizer 2←

↑

Tableau 3

x_1	x_2	s_1	s_2	s_3	b	
4	6	0	0	0	0	c row
4	6	2	0	2	26	z row
0	0	2	0	2	26	$z - c$ row
						Basic Variables
0	1	1	0	−1	3	x_2 Barley
0	0	2	1	−5	3	s_2 Slack labor
1	0	−1	0	2	2	x_1 Wheat

will be costless, so that the z-row coefficients for both x_1 and x_2 in Tableau 1 are zero.

Rule 1C. Subtracting c from z for a particular activity yields a measure of the *net* profit accruing per unit to that activity, with its sign changed.

Thus, the $z - c$-row coefficient of -6 for x_2 in Tableau 1 indicates that introduction of 1 bushel of barley into the basis would cause a net increase of $6 in profit. As we have already noted, for existing basic variables in any tableau the $z - c$-row coefficients must always be zero.

Rule 1D. Activity x_2 has the largest negative $z - c$-row coefficient, i.e., -6, hence it is selected as the activity to enter the basis at iteration 1. Mark its column in Tableau 1 with a vertical arrow ($\uparrow$).

Rule 2A. Having chosen the activity to enter the basis, we now divide each entry in its column into the b-column element of the same row. This gives the coefficients of the R column, measuring directly the greatest number of units of the introduced activity that could be brought into the solution if each constraint in turn were the only effective one in the matrix. Thus in Tableau 1 of Table 13.1, with 8 acres of land available, for example, and with barley requiring 2 acres per bushel, the amount of barley that could be produced if land only were limiting is $\frac{8}{2} = 4$ bushels. The R-column values for s_2 and s_3 are $\frac{12}{1} = 12$ bushels and $\frac{5}{1} = 5$ bushels respectively.

Rule 2B. The smallest R value in Tableau 1 is 4, indicating that barley production may be expanded to 4 bushels, at which point the most limiting constraint, land, is met. We therefore choose s_1, slack land, as the basic variable to leave the basis.

Rules 3 to 5. Complete iteration 1 by transforming the tableau according to rules 3 to 5 of Chapter 12. The resultant matrix is shown in Tableau 2 of Table 13.1.

Iteration 2

Rule 1A. As above.

Rule 1B. As above. Recall from section 5.3 that the method for calculating the z-row coefficients should be applied to the b column as well as to the columns in the body of the tableau. In this way total profit earned by the current solution is calculated. In Tableau 2 of Table 13.1, for instance, we apply the z-row calculation rules to the b column and obtain the following expression for total profit:

$$\text{(4bu. } x_2 \times \$6 \text{ per bushel)} + \text{(8 m-hrs. } s_2 \times \$0 \text{ per man-hour)}$$
$$+ \text{(1 cwt. } s_3 \times \$0 \text{ per cwt.)} = \$24$$

Rule 1C. As above. Again note that this rule is carried through to the b column. We assume that the c-row entry in the b column is always zero, hence $z - c$ for this column always equals z, which is just calculated as the total profit earned by activities in the given solution. Thus in Tableau 2, the $z - c$-row element for the b column equals $24.

Rule 1D. x_1, having the largest negative $z - c$ value, is chosen to enter the basis at iteration 2.

Rule 2A.   The R column, working downward, is calculated as

$$\frac{4}{\frac{1}{2}} = 8 \qquad \frac{8}{2\frac{1}{2}} = 3\frac{1}{5} \qquad \frac{1}{\frac{1}{2}} = 2$$

Rule 2B.   The first constraint to be encountered in expanding x_1 will be that corresponding to s_3, the fertilizer restriction, since it has the smallest R value. This constraint permits an increase of only 2 bushels in wheat production. Therefore the variable s_3, slack fertilizer, is chosen to leave the basis.

Rules 3 to 5.   As before, application of rules 3 to 5 completes the transformation of the tableau through iteration 2.

Iteration 3

Rule 1A.   As above.

Rule 1B.   As above. Note the effect of negative a_{ij} elements in the calculation of the z row. The nonbasic variable s_1 (slack land) has both positive and negative a_{ij} elements in its column in Tableau 3, so we shall use it as illustration. If a unit of s_1 were to be introduced into the solution in Tableau 3:

a. The level of x_2 would *decrease* by 1 bushel of barley per acre of slack land introduced (a_{ij} coefficient positive).

b. The level of s_2 would *decrease* by 2 man-hours per acre of slack land introduced (a_{ij} coefficient positive).

c. The level of x_1 would *increase* by 1 bushel of wheat per acre of slack land introduced (a_{ij} coefficient negative).

The costs of these changes are calculated, per acre of slack land introduced, as

$$(1 \text{ bu. } x_2 \times \$6 \text{ per bushel}) + (2 \text{ m-hrs. } s_2 \times \$0 \text{ per man-hour})$$
$$+(-1 \text{ bu. } x_1 \times \$4 \text{ per bushel}) = \$2 \text{ per acre}$$

Rule 1C.   As above.

Rule 1D.   All $z-c$-row elements are zero or positive, hence no variable can be introduced into the solution which will increase profit. The basis contained in Tableau 3 is therefore optimal.

13.3   Direct Modification
of the $z-c$ Row

Having given in the above rules the details of calculation of the z row in order to form the $z-c$ row for any tableau, we now reveal that this full calculation is unnecessary. While an understanding of the full computation is desirable for a complete appreciation of the meaning of the

$z - c$-row coefficients, in fact the $z - c$ row of any tableau may be calculated *directly* from the $z - c$ row of the previous tableau by applying to it the same rules as are applied for the modification of any other row in the old tableau. For the *initial* tableau, the $z - c$ row is written in the usual way; since the initial basis is generally formed from slack and/or artificial activities having zero c-row values, the $z - c$-row coefficients for the real variables in the initial tableau are simply the negatives of their own c-row coefficients. For example, the c-row coefficients of x_1 and x_2 in Tableau 1 of Table 13.1 are 4 and 6 respectively, hence their $z - c$-row values are -4 and -6 respectively.

To illustrate the direct transformation of the $z - c$ row, let us apply rule 5 from Chapter 12 to the $z - c$ row of Tableau 1 in Table 13.1. The "incoming row" for iteration 1 is:

$$\tfrac{1}{2} \quad 1 \quad \tfrac{1}{2} \quad 0 \quad 0 \quad 4$$

and the coefficient of the $z - c$ row in the x_2 column, i.e., the outgoing column, is -6. Thus the elements of the new $z - c$ row can be calculated by applying the rule 5 formula, as follows:

Coefficient in Tableau 1	$-$	Outgoing Column Element	$\times$	Incoming Row Element	$=$	Coefficient in Tableau 2
-4	$-$	$(-6$	$\times$	$\tfrac{1}{2})$	$=$	-1
-6	$-$	$(-6$	$\times$	$1)$	$=$	0
0	$-$	$(-6$	$\times$	$\tfrac{1}{2})$	$=$	3
0	$-$	$(-6$	$\times$	$0)$	$=$	0
0	$-$	$(-6$	$\times$	$0)$	$=$	0
0	$-$	$(-6$	$\times$	$4)$	$=$	24

The reader may reaffirm the validity of this operation by calculating the $z - c$ row of Tableau 3 from that of Tableau 2 in this example, using the same procedures.

Henceforth, in transforming matrixes, we shall use this short cut to avoid writing the z row for each tableau.

13.4 Further Examination of Rule 1

13.4.1 Greatest Unit Increase in Profit

We can easily demonstrate that, in selecting the variable to enter the basis, the one that will give the greatest *unit* increase in total profit will not necessarily also lead to the greatest *total* increase in profit at that iteration.

Figure 13.1 depicts a problem with two activities, maize and beans, and two constraints, land and labor.

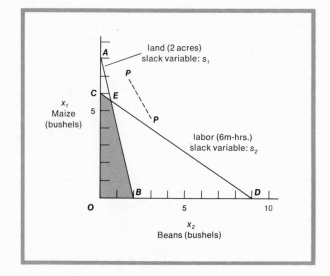

Figure 13.1

Let x_1 = number of bushels of maize production
$\quad x_2$ = number of bushels of bean production
$\quad s_1$ = acres of slack land
$\quad s_2$ = man-hours of slack labor
Tableau 1 of Table 13.2 represents the initial matrix for this problem.

Using rule 1 we choose x_2 to enter the basis, giving an increase in total profit of $10 per bushel. Introduction of the beans activity moves the basis to point B in Figure 13.1. The new tableau is Tableau 2 of Table 13.2. We observe that the total profit in this plan is $20, which is of course the value of the two bushels of beans introduced into the solution.

Suppose instead that we had disobeyed rule 1D and introduced x_1 at iteration 1. The effect is shown in Table 13.3. Observe that the basis moves from O to C in Figure 13.1, an increase of 6 bushels of maize at $6 per bushel. Thus the total profit earned by the solution in Tableau 2 of Table 13.3 is $36.

It is therefore apparent that at any iteration rule 1D does not necessarily lead to the greatest *total* increase in profit. But consistent application of the rule does eventually lead to the optimum vertex for any given problem.

13.4.2 Shortest Route to Optimum Vertex

In addition it is possible to see that rule 1 will not necessarily lead to the optimum by the fastest possible route. Again an illustration should clarify this point.

169

TABLE 13.2

Tableau 1

Real Variables		Slack Variables				
Maize	Beans	Land	Labor			
x_1	x_2	s_1	s_2	b		
-6	-10	0	0	0	$z - c$ row	R
					Basic Variables	
$\frac{1}{4}$	①	1	0	2	s_1 Slack land	$2\leftarrow$
1	$\frac{2}{3}$	0	1	6	s_2 Slack labor	9
	$\uparrow$					

Tableau 2

x_1	x_2	s_1	s_2	b	$z - c$ row
$-3\frac{1}{2}$	0	10	0	20	
					Basic Variables
$\frac{1}{4}$	1	1	0	2	x_2 Beans
$\frac{5}{6}$	0	$-\frac{2}{3}$	1	$4\frac{2}{3}$	s_2 Slack labor

TABLE 13.3

Tableau 1

Real Variables		Slack Variables				
Maize	Beans	Land	Labor			
x_1	x_2	s_1	s_2	b		
-6	-10	0	0	0	$z - c$ row	R
					Basic Variables	
$\frac{1}{4}$	1	1	0	2	s_1 Slack land	8
①	$\frac{2}{3}$	0	1	6	s_2 Slack labor	$6\leftarrow$
$\uparrow$						

Tableau 2

x_1	x_2	s_1	s_2	b	
0	-6	0	6	36	$z - c$ row
					Basic Variables
0	$\frac{5}{6}$	1	$-\frac{1}{4}$	$\frac{1}{2}$	s_1 Slack land
1	$\frac{2}{3}$	0	1	6	x_1 Maize

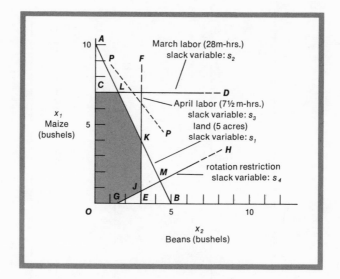

Figure 13.2

Using again a maize-and-beans profit maximization problem, we can construct the hypothetical situation shown in Figure 13.2. Tableau 1 in Table 13.4 shows the initial matrix for this problem. The supplies of land, March labor, and April labor limit production, and a further rotational restriction specifies that for each bushel of beans production in excess of $1\frac{1}{2}$ bushels, there must be at least $\frac{1}{2}$ bushel of maize. The reader should verify carefully the correspondence of each constraint in Figure 13.2 with the appropriate row in Tableau 1 of Table 13.4.

With profit coefficients of $5 per bushel for maize and $6 per bushel for beans, the optimum vertex can be calculated graphically as L in Figure 13.2.

Application of the conventional simplex rules to this problem yields the solution sequence shown in Table 13.4 and verifies the graphical solution found above in which the values of the real variables are x_1 (maize) $= 7$ bushels and x_2 (beans) $= 1\frac{1}{2}$ bushels. Notice that the solution follows the path on Figure 13.2 of O, G, J, K, L (represented by Tableaux 1, 2, 3, 4, 5 respectively of Table 13.4). Solution by this means takes four iterations.

Now suppose we *disobey* the rule to select the activity to enter the basis at the first iteration. Rather than choosing x_2 as dictated by rule 1, let us introduce x_1 instead. This will move the solution up the vertical axis to C, shown as Tableau 2 in Table 13.5. Then applying the normal rules, we proceed with the calculation and reach the optimal vertex L, as shown in Tableau 3 on Table 13.5. (Compare this with Tableau 5 of Table 13.4.)[1] Notice that finding the optimum by the route followed in Table 13.5 required only two iterations.

[1] Note that the order of rows in these final tableaux is different. Why?

TABLE 13.4
Tableau 1

| | Real Variables | | Slack Variables | | | | | | | |
| | Maize | Beans | Land | March Labor | April Labor | Rotation | | | | |
	x_1	x_2	s_1	s_2	s_3	s_4	b			R
$z - c$ row	−5	−6	0	0	0	0	0			
									Basic Variables	
	½	1	1	0	0	0	5		s_1 Slack land	5
	4	0	0	1	0	0	28		s_2 Slack March labor	—
	0	2½	0	0	1	0	7½		s_3 Slack April labor	3
	−2	①	0	0	0	1	1½		s_4 Slack rotation	1½ ←

↑

Tableau 2

	x_1	x_2	s_1	s_2	s_3	s_4	b			R
$z - c$ row	−17	0	0	0	0	6	9			
									Basic Variables	
	2½	0	1	0	0	−1	3½		s_1 Slack land	1⅖
	4	0	0	1	0	0	28		s_2 Slack March labor	7
	⑤	0	0	0	1	−2½	3¾		s_3 Slack April labor	¾ ←
	−2	1	0	0	0	1	1½		x_2 Beans	—

↑

Tableau 3

x_1	x_2	s_1	s_2	s_3	s_4	b	$z - c$ row	R
0	0	0	0	$3\frac{2}{5}$	$-2\frac{1}{2}$	$21\frac{3}{4}$		
							Basic Variables	
0	0	1	0	$-\frac{1}{2}$	$\frac{1}{4}$	$1\frac{5}{8}$	s_1 Slack land	$6\frac{1}{2}$ ←
0	0	0	1	$-\frac{4}{5}$	2	25	s_2 Slack March labor	$12\frac{1}{2}$
1	0	0	0	$\frac{1}{5}$	$-\frac{1}{2}$	$\frac{3}{4}$	x_1 Maize	—
0	1	0	0	$\frac{2}{5}$	0	3	x_2 Beans	—

Tableau 4

x_1	x_2	s_1	s_2	s_3	s_4	b	$z - c$ row	R
0	0	10	0	$-1\frac{3}{5}$	0	38		
							Basic Variables	
0	0	4	0	-2	1	$6\frac{1}{2}$	s_4 Slack rotation	$3\frac{3}{4}$ ←
0	0	-8	1	$3\frac{1}{5}$	0	12	s_2 Slack March labor	—
1	0	2	0	$-\frac{4}{5}$	0	4	x_1 Maize	—
0	1	0	0	$\frac{2}{5}$	0	3	x_2 Beans	$7\frac{1}{2}$

Tableau 5

x_1	x_2	s_1	s_2	s_3	s_4	b	Basic Variables
0	0	6	½	0	0	44	$z - c$ row
0	0	-1	⅝	0	1	14	s_4 Slack rotation
0	0	$-2½$	5/16	1	0	3¾	s_3 Slack April labor
1	0	0	¼	0	0	7	x_1 Maize
0	1	1	$-⅛$	0	0	1½	x_2 Beans

TABLE 13.5

Tableau 1

	Real Variables		Slack Variables						
	Maize	Beans	Land	March Labor	April Labor	Rotation		z − c row	
Basic Variables	x_1	x_2	s_1	s_2	s_3	s_4	b		R
	−5	−6	0	0	0	0	0	z − c row	
s_1 Slack land	½	1	1	0	0	0	5		10
s_2 Slack March labor	④	1	0	1	0	0	28		7←
s_3 Slack April labor	0	2½	0	0	1	0	7½		—
s_4 Slack rotation	−2	1	0	0	0	1	1½		—

↑

Tableau 2

	Maize	Beans	Land	March Labor	April Labor	Rotation		z − c row	
Basic Variables	x_1	x_2	s_1	s_2	s_3	s_4	b		R
	0	−6	0	1¼	0	0	35	z − c row	
s_1 Slack land	0	①	1	−⅛	0	0	1½		1½←
x_1 Maize	1	0	0	¼	0	0	7		—
s_3 Slack April labor	0	2½	0	0	1	0	7½		3
s_4 Slack rotation	0	1	0	½	0	1	15½		15½

↑

175

Tableau 3

x_1	x_2	s_1	s_2	s_3	s_4	b	
0	0	6	½	0	0	44	$z - c$ row
0	1	1	$-\frac{1}{8}$	0	0	1½	x_2 Beans
1	0	0	$\frac{1}{4}$	0	0	7	x_1 Maize
0	0	$-2\frac{1}{2}$	$\frac{5}{16}$	1	0	3¾	s_3 Slack April labor
0	0	-1	$\frac{5}{8}$	0	1	14	s_4 Slack rotation

This illustration demonstrates that our formal set of simplex rules will not necessarily lead us to the optimal vertex by the quickest possible route. However, it is generally impossible to ascertain easily whether it would pay to disobey the set rules during the course of solution of a given problem. Alternative procedures for selecting the variables to enter and leave the basis at any iteration have been suggested, but none has yet been developed which leads to any consistent improvement in the number of iterations required for the solution of linear programming problems. Thus we shall continue to use the rules derived above, appreciating that the path over which they lead us may not be the shortest, but certainly will land us at the optimum vertex in due course.

13.5 Further Examination of Rule 2

13.5.1 Zero a_{ij} Coefficients

As we have seen, for each row in a given tableau the R column shows the greatest number of units of the already chosen incoming activity which could enter the basis if that row were the only one in the tableau. By choosing that variable whose R value is smallest, rule 2 selects to leave the basis that activity which most limits the expansion of the incoming activity.

We have seen that the R column is calculated by dividing for each row the b-column element by the a_{ij} element in the incoming activity column. What is the significance of *zero* a_{ij} coefficients in the calculation of the R column? For example, in Tableau 1 of Table 13.4, where x_2 (beans) is chosen to enter the basis, what is the R value for s_2, the March labor slack variable? We should calculate the R value as $28 \div 0$ which equals infinity.[2] From this we infer that if March labor were the only constraint in the problem, production of beans could be expanded to infinity. To see whether this is so, refer to Figure 13.2. The zero a_{ij} coefficient for x_2 with respect to March labor signifies that the March labor constraint line CD is *parallel to* the x_2 axis and therefore does not meet it until infinity.

Thus in calculating the R column we may skip over any zero a_{ij} coefficients, as we know that the basic variable of that row will not limit expansion of the introduced activity.

13.5.2 Negative a_{ij} Coefficients

An example of a negative a_{ij} coefficient is provided in the x_1 column in Tableau 1 in Table 13.5. Selection of this maize activity to enter the basis at the first iteration will move the solution from O up the vertical axis in

---

[2] More strictly, no number exists which, when multiplied by zero, gives 28.

Figure 13.2. We notice that because of the negative coefficient, -2, in the s_4 row, the line GH corresponding to this rotational constraint slopes *away from* the x_1 axis. (Compare the April labor constraint line FE, which is parallel to the vertical axis because the corresponding coefficient—at the intersection of the x_1 column and the s_3 row—is zero, as considered in the previous section.)

Thus, if the rotational restriction were the only one in the problem and x_1 were introduced into the basis, beans production could be expanded to infinity. The rotational restriction provides no constraint whatsoever on expansion of beans production.

Strictly calculating an R value from a positive b coefficient and a negative a_{ij} coefficient leads to a finite (negative) number: in the case of x_2 and s_4 in Tableau 1 of Table 13.5 we obtain $R = 1\frac{1}{2} \div -2 = -\frac{3}{4}$. However, we must eliminate this number from consideration when we are selecting the smallest R value, since, as we have seen, the variable for whose row it occurs does not limit expansion of the introduced activity. More simply, in computing the R column at any iteration, a row containing a negative a_{ij} can be skipped, just as zero a_{ij} coefficients are also skipped.

13.5.3 Infinite Solutions

From the discussions of the previous two sections we can confirm the conclusions of section 9.3, in which infinite solutions were considered. There we saw that if all the a_{ij} coefficients in the column of an activity selected for introduction into the basis are either zero or negative, no variable in the problem limits expansion of that activity, which could therefore be introduced into the basis at an infinite level, increasing profit to infinity.

In the light of the subsequent treatment of the simplex, the reader should be sure he fully understands the examples of infinite solutions given in section 9.3.

13.5.4 Degeneracy

Having considered the effects on the calculation of R of negative and zero elements in the body of the matrix, we turn to the existence of negative or zero elements in the b column. In the normal simplex procedure, negative elements should not appear in the b column (since they indicate an infeasible basis); let us therefore consider only *zero* b-column coefficients. As we have seen in section 9.4, zero coefficient(s) in the b column indicates a degenerate solution, i.e., one or more basic variables present in the solution at zero level.

In computing a particular R column it is apparent that if a b-column element of zero is divided by a positive a_{ij} coefficient, the resultant R value must be zero and *must* be the smallest in the column (since negative

R values do not exist). Hence its corresponding variable *must* be chosen to leave the basis, unless of course it "ties" with one or more other zero R-column values, in which case any of the corresponding variables may be selected, as we have seen, in order to break the tie.

To illustrate, refer to the first example used for the discussion of degeneracy in Chapter 9. The diagram for this problem is given in Figure 9.5, and its full simplex solution is shown in Table 9.4. At the first iteration, x_1 (cows) is chosen to enter the basis and the R values are calculated as $0/3 = 0$ for s_1, and $5/1 = 5$ for s_2. Thus, in terms of rule 2, we see that s_1 permits the smallest increase in x_1 at iteration 1; in fact it allows *no* increase in x_1. Introduction of x_1 to replace s_1 exhibits the characteristic features of degeneracy, which have already been examined in section 9.4.

The next matrix in the same problem (Tableau 2 of Table 9.4) further illustrates the degeneracy problem. In this case, in calculating the R column corresponding to the introduced variable x_2 (oats), we do not obtain any zero R values, even though there is a b-column entry of zero (corresponding to x_1). The reason is that in the column of this introduced variable the a_{ij} coefficient corresponding to the x_1 row is *negative* and is therefore skipped in the calculation of R. In other words because of the coefficient $-2/3$ at the intersection of the x_2 column and the x_1 row of Tableau 2, we infer that variable x_1 does not constrain the expansion of x_2 in any way, and hence x_1 cannot be selected to leave the basis. There remains only one other candidate to leave the basis (viz., the slack land activity, s_2), and since it has a "normal" positive R value, it is duly selected; the calculations then proceed to Tableau 3, which turns out to be the optimum solution.

13.5.5 Shorter Routes to the Optimum Vertex

In section 13.4.2 we saw an example in which infringement of rule 1 actually led to a speedier solution. Now the same problem can be used to illustrate that acting contrary to rule 2 may also in special circumstances allow quicker convergence on the optimum vertex.

Table 13.6 shows again the initial matrix for this problem. Using rule 1 the beans activity x_2 is selected from Tableau 1 to enter the basis at the first iteration. The R column is calculated as usual and is shown on the right-hand side of the tableau.

Now suppose, instead of choosing the activity with the smallest R value, we deliberately select s_1, slack land, to leave the basis, knowing that this will cause the basis to move to point B in Figure 13.2. We can see from the diagram that the basis at B will be infeasible (i.e., will contain some negative variables). We can deduce this also from Tableau 1, since we know that choosing any activity to leave the basis whose R value is *not* the smallest will cause the solution to stray into the infeasible region.

TABLE 13.6
Tableau 1

	Real Variables		Slack Variables				b	Basic Variables		R
	Maize	Beans	Land	March Labor	April Labor	Rotation				
	x_1	x_2	s_1	s_2	s_3	s_4				
$z - c$ row	-5	-6	0	0	0	0	0			
	½	①	1	0	0	0	5	s_1	Slack land	5←
	4	0	0	1	0	0	28	s_2	Slack March labor	—
	0	2½	0	0	1	0	7½	s_3	Slack April labor	3
	-2	1	0	0	0	1	1½	s_4	Slack rotation	1½
		↑								

Tableau 2

	x_1	x_2	s_1	s_2	s_3	s_4	b	Basic Variables		R
$z - c$ row	-2	0	6	0	0	0	30			
	½	1	1	0	0	0	5	x_2	Beans	10
	④	0	0	1	0	0	28	s_2	Slack March labor	7←
	$-1¼$	0	$-2½$	0	1	0	-5	s_3	Slack April labor	—
	$-2½$	0	-1	0	0	1	$-3½$	s_4	Slack rotation	—
	↑									

Tableau 3

x_1	x_2	s_1	s_2	s_3	s_4	b	Basic Variables
0	0	6	$\frac{1}{2}$	0	0	44	$z - c$ row
0	1	1	$-\frac{1}{8}$	0	0	$1\frac{1}{2}$	x_2 Beans
1	0	0	$\frac{1}{4}$	0	0	7	x_1 Maize
0	0	$-2\frac{1}{2}$	$\frac{5}{16}$	1	0	$3\frac{3}{4}$	s_3 Slack April labor
0	0	-1	$\frac{5}{8}$	0	1	14	s_4 Slack rotation

181

Nevertheless, calculating iteration 1 by replacing s_1 with x_2 in the basis leads us to Tableau 2. The reader may verify that the values of variables in this solution correspond to point B on Figure 13.2. Performing the next iteration in the conventional manner, we introduce x_1, maize, into the basis and eliminate s_2, slack March labor. This moves the solution up the constraint line AB from B to L, which is the optimal vertex. The final matrix is shown in Tableau 3. Solution of the problem by this means took two iterations, compared with four iterations when the conventional procedure was used.

The conclusion is similar to that reached in section 13.4.2. Routes to the optimum vertex may exist which are shorter than that followed by the conventional simplex method.

EXERCISES

1. The following is the tableau obtained after the first iteration in the ordinary simplex solution of a maximization problem:

Tableau 2

x_1	x_2	x_3	s_1	s_2	b	
-5	60	0	25	0	150	$z - c$ row
						Basic Variables
$\frac{1}{2}$	$1\frac{1}{2}$	1	$\frac{1}{2}$	0	3	x_3
$-\frac{1}{2}$	$-2\frac{1}{2}$	0	$-\frac{1}{2}$	1	12	s_2

What was the *initial* basic solution for this problem? What are the net profit coefficients (i.e., the c row)? How far could each real variable (x_1, x_2, x_3) expand if the constraint whose slack variable is s_1 were omitted from this problem?

2. Determine the optimal solution for the problem in exercise 1. Could this solution have been found in fewer iterations? How?

3. Use the long method (see section 5.3) for calculation of the z row in Tableau 3 of the above exercise. Verify that the $z - c$ row calculated in this way is the same as that found by direct modification of the $z - c$ row in Tableau 2.

4. For the following set of maximum constraints:

$$-x_1 + x_2 \leq 0$$
$$x_1 - 4x_2 \leq 2$$

use the simplex procedure to find an optimum solution if the objective function is:

a. Maximize

$$z = 2x_1 + x_2$$

b. Maximize

$$z = x_1 + 2x_2$$

5. Referring to exercise 4 of Chapter 8, suppose that a pair of trousers returns $5 and a suit $11. With the other assumptions in this problem remaining the same, use the simplex to determine an optimal solution.

6. Show that the path followed by the ordinary simplex in exercise 5 is not the quickest route to the optimum vertex. Perform the simplex calculations that optimize the solution in the fewest possible iterations.

14

COMPUTATIONAL
ASPECTS OF THE SIMPLEX
WITH ARTIFICIAL VARIABLES

14.1 Orientation

In Part II artificial variables were introduced and their interpretation and use were discussed in some detail. In section 6.2 it was shown that a problem containing minimum (and/or equality) constraints will generally not provide a first feasible basis when the initial tableau is set up. Thus, as shown in section 6.3, a new variable, an artificial variable, can be added to each such constraint in the problem, thereby yielding an initial basis. The two-phase simplex may be used in the solution of these problems. In phase I of this method, the artificial variables are forced out of the basis; if a feasible solution to the problem exists, it will be obtained when all artificial variables are nonbasic and therefore zero. Phase II of the simplex may then be applied in the usual way to the tableau from the end of phase I, leading eventually to the optimal solution. The logic of this procedure was outlined in section 6.5. In some problems the constraints are such that no feasible solution exists; the termination of phase I will indicate this quite simply, as shown in section 9.2.2.

A problem containing two real activities and six constraints, of which three required artificial variables, was solved in Chapter 10 to illustrate the application of computers to linear programming problems: in the appendix to that chapter the full set of tableaux obtained during the solution of the problem were set out, although all computational details were not discussed. It is now our task, having considered in the previous three chapters the computational aspects of the straightforward simplex, to turn to the two-phase simplex and finalize the treatment of its mechanics. In this chapter we shall use two examples. As the first illustration we shall take the simple minimization problem from Chapter 2 and solve it by using the two-phase simplex. We will be able to compare our simplex solution with the graphical treatments of this problem considered earlier, just as we did in Chapters 11–13 for our wheat/barley maximization problem. As the second illustration we shall use the above-mentioned problem from Chapter 10.

14.2 Setting Up the Matrix

By now the reader is familiar with the method of taking the coefficients of a problem written out extensively in the form "maximize/minimize . . . subject to . . ." and transferring them to an initial tableau. In relation to the two-phase simplex, the main detail yet to be covered is the construction of the "artificial criterion row." Let us, then, examine the setting up of the initial tableaux of our examples.

14.2.1 Example 1

Recall that the problem is one of determining the number of tons of cornmeal (x_1) and fishmeal (x_2) which minimize total costs, subject to the condition that the resultant mix meets certain minimum specifications on the content of protein, oil, and fiber. Numerically the problem is written as follows:

Minimize

$$z = 3x_1 + 5x_2 \qquad (14.1a)$$

subject to

$$
\begin{aligned}
1x_1 + 1x_2 &\geq 4 \text{ (minimum protein requirement)} \\
1x_1 + 3x_2 &\geq 6 \text{ (minimum oil requirement)} \\
7x_1 &\geq 14 \text{ (minimum fiber requirement)}
\end{aligned}
\qquad (14.1b)
$$

and
$$x_1, x_2 \geq 0 \qquad (14.1c)$$

Adding nonnegative surplus variables s_1, s_2, and s_3 and artificial variables s_1', s_2', and s_3' corresponding to the protein, oil, and fiber constraints respectively, we obtain the following set of constraint equations:

$$
\begin{aligned}
1x_1 + 1x_2 - 1s_1 && + 1s_1' && &= 4 \\
1x_1 + 3x_2 && - 1s_2 && + 1s_2' && &= 6 \\
7x_1 && && - 1s_3 && + 1s_3' &= 14
\end{aligned}
\qquad (14.2)
$$

The basic variables in the initial tableau, then, are the three artificial activities, which appear in the basis at levels of $s_1' = 4$, $s_2' = 6$, and $s_3' = 14$. This matrix is shown as Tableau 1 in Table 14.1.

Observe the construction of the $z - c$ row at the top of the tableau. Recall the convention outlined in section 6.1 about the signs of c-row coefficients. There we agreed always to write profits as positive c-row coefficients and costs as negative, and to set up tableaux in maximization form. This means that in the present problem, instead of minimizing costs, we will in fact be *maximizing* the *negative* of costs which, as already shown, is an exactly equivalent problem. Equation (14.1a) shows that cornmeal costs \$3 per ton and fishmeal costs \$5 per ton. Thus we write the *cost* coefficients as -3 and -5 in the c row for the x_1 and x_2 columns respectively in Tableau 1. Since no costs attach to any of the surplus or artificial activities, all the remaining c-row coefficients in Tableau 1 are zero.

The z row, as we know, measures for any nonbasic activity the costs associated with changes in the values of currently basic variables as a result of the introduction of a unit of that nonbasic activity into the solution. Introduction of x_1 or x_2 into the basis in Tableau 1 would cause the levels of s_1', s_2', and s_3' to change, but since the c-row coefficients of these artificial variables are zero, such changes will be costless. Hence the z-row coefficients for x_1 and x_2, as for all other variables in Tableau 1, are zero. Likewise, total costs at this combination of activities are zero, hence the coefficient at the intersection of the z row and the b column is also zero.

The $z - c$ row is calculated as usual by subtracting the c row from the z row. Because of the assumptions under which the initial tableau is set up, the $z - c$-row coefficient for any variable in the initial tableau is simply the negative of its c-row coefficient, as we found in section 13.3. In subsequent tableaux computed during the solution of the problem we will not write the c row and the z row in full; we shall simply calculate the $z - c$ row in any tableau directly from that of the previous tableau following the argument stated in section 13.3.

Turning now to the artificial criterion row, we derive it by using exactly the same techniques as applied above to calculate the "real" $z - c$ row. But the $z' - c'$ row will differ from the $z - c$ row insofar as the c' row contains different coefficients from the c row.

In the c' row we assign a zero "profit" to all variables in the tableau except the artificial activities. We attribute to the latter a profit coefficient of -1, thereby ensuring that when we have maximized profit, no artificial variable will appear in the solution (if a feasible solution to the problem exists). Thus the c' row at the bottom of Tableau 1 is written as shown.

Next the z' row is calculated. Like the real z row it measures for any nonbasic variable the costs associated with changes in the values of currently basic variables as a result of introduction of a unit of that nonbasic activity into the solution. We know that introduction of x_1, x_2, or any of the surplus variables s_1, s_2, s_3 into the basis in Tableau 1 will cause

TABLE 14.1

Phase I

Tableau 1

	Real Variables		Slack Variables			Artificial Variables					
	Cornmeal	Fishmeal	Protein	Oil	Fiber	Protein	Oil	Fiber			
	x_1	x_2	s_1	s_2	s_3	s_1'	s_2'	s_3'	b		
	-3	-5	0	0	0	0	0	0	0		c row
	0	0	0	0	0	0	0	0	0		z row
	3	5	0	0	0	0	0	0	0	R	$z - c$ row
											Basic Variables
	1	1	-1	0	0	1	0	0	4	4	s_1' Artificial (protein)
	1	3	0	-1	0	0	1	0	6	6	s_2' Artificial (oil)
	⑦	0	0	0	-1	0	0	1	14	2←	s_3' Artificial (fiber)
	0	0	0	0	0	0	0	0	0		c' row
	-9	-4	1	1	1	-1	-1	-1	-24		z' row
	-9	-4	1	1	1	-1	-1	0	-24		$z' - c'$ row
	↑										

Tableau 2

	x_1	x_2	s_1	s_2	s_3	s_1'	s_2'	s_3'	b		R
$z - c$ row	0	5	0	0	$3/7$	0	0		-6		
										Basic Variables	
	0	1	-1	0	$1/7$	1	0		2	s_1' Artificial (protein)	2
	0	③	0	-1	$1/7$	0	1		4	s_2' Artificial (oil)	$1\frac{1}{3}$ ←
	1	0	0	0	$-1/7$	0	0		2	x_1 Cornmeal	—
$z' - c'$ row	0	-4	1	1	$-2/7$	0	0		-6		

↑

Tableau 3

	x_1	x_2	s_1	s_2	s_3	s_1'	s_2'	s_3'	b		R
$z - c$ row	0	0	0	$1\frac{2}{3}$	$4/21$	0			$-12\frac{2}{3}$		
										Basic Variables	
	0	0	-1	(1/3)	$2/21$	1			$2/3$	s_1' Artificial (protein)	2 ←
	0	1	0	$-1/3$	$1/21$	0			$1\frac{1}{3}$	x_2 Fishmeal	—
	1	0	0	0	$-1/7$	0			2	x_1 Cornmeal	—
$z' - c'$ row	0	0	1	$-1/3$	$-2/21$	0			$-2/3$		

↑

Tableau 4

x_1	x_2	s_1	s_2	s_3	s_1'	s_2'	s_3	b	Basic Variables	R
0	0	5	0	$-\frac{2}{7}$				-16	$z - c$ row	
									Basic Variables	
0	0	-3	1	$\left(\frac{2}{7}\right)$				2	s_2 Surplus oil	$7\leftarrow$
0	1	-1	0	$\frac{1}{7}$				2	x_2 Fishmeal	14
1	0	0	0	$-\frac{1}{7}$				2	x_1 Cornmeal	—
0	0	0	0	0				0	$z' - c'$ row	

$\uparrow$

Phase II
Tableau 5

x_1	x_2	s_1	s_2	s_3	s_1'	s_2'	s_3'	b	Basic Variables
0	0	2	1	0				-14	$z - c$ row
									Basic Variables
0	0	$-10\frac{1}{2}$	$3\frac{1}{2}$	1				7	s_3 Surplus fiber
0	1	$\frac{1}{2}$	$-\frac{1}{2}$	0				1	x_2 Fishmeal
1	0	$-1\frac{1}{2}$	$\frac{1}{2}$	0				3	x_1 Cornmeal

changes in the values of one or more of the presently basic variables s'_1, s'_2, s'_3. Furthermore, these latter variables *do* have nonzero c'-row coefficients, hence there *will* be costs (measured in terms of our artificial profit) incurred through changes in their values. Refer, for instance, to the x_2 column in Tableau 1 of Table 14.1. The "displacement coefficients," or a_{ij} coefficients, in its column denote the amount by which the value of each basic variable will change per unit of x_2 introduced into the solution. Reading down the column we see that for each ton of fishmeal introduced into the basis, 1 unit of s'_1, 3 units of s'_2 and 0 units of s'_3 would be displaced. The costs of such displacement, per ton of x_2 introduced, can be calculated by multiplying these a_{ij} coefficients by the c'-row coefficients of the relevant basic variables, in just the same way as we normally calculate the real z row. Units of s'_1, s'_2, and s'_3 each return an artificial profit of $\$-1$, hence the total costs resulting from the introduction of 1 ton of x_2 into the basis would be

$$
\begin{array}{lr}
1 \text{ unit } s'_1 \times \$-1 \text{ per unit} & = \$-1 \\
3 \text{ units } s'_2 \times \$-1 \text{ per unit} & = \$-3 \\
0 \text{ units } s'_3 \times \$-1 \text{ per unit} & = \$\ \ 0 \\
\hline
\text{TOTAL "COSTS"} & = \$-4
\end{array}
$$

This calculation gives the z'-row coefficient for x_2 in Tableau 1. The reader should compare the above method of deriving the z' row with that for the z row given in section 5.3, to verify that the techniques used are absolutely identical. He should then practice its application by checking the derivation of all other z'-row coefficients in Tableau 1 of Table 14.1.

Notice in particular that the z'-row coefficients for the s'_1, $s,'_2$ and s'_3 columns equal the corresponding c'-row coefficient. As we have seen in the case of real z and c rows, this always occurs for the columns of basic variables, and hence in this case also leads to a $z' - c'$-row coefficient of zero.

Note also that, as usual, the identical rules for calculation of z'-row coefficients are applied to the b column. Just as this procedure with the real z row leads to a coefficient for the total profit (cost) earned by the current basis, so do we derive in the z' row a measure of the total artificial profit of the present solution. In Tableau 1 of Table 14.1, for instance, we have 4 units s'_1 earning a profit of $\$-1$ per unit, 6 units of s'_2 earning $\$-1$ pre unit, and 14 units of s'_3 earning $\$-1$ per unit. Total artificial profit is therefore $\$(4 \times -1) + (6 \times -1) + (14 \times -1) = \$-24$.

We proceed finally to compute the $z' - c'$-row coefficients, formed in the usual way by subtraction of the c' row from the z' row. As we expect, the negative of the $z' - c'$-row coefficient for each activity indicates by how much total profit would be increased through the introduction of one unit of that activity. Thus, introduction of 1 ton of cornmeal, x_1, into the basis of Tableau 1 would *increase* profit by \$9 ($z' - c'$-row coefficient *negative*); similarly if a unit of surplus oil, s_2, were introduced, profit would be *decreased* by \$1 ($z' - c'$-row coefficient *positive*).

A simplification of the procedure for calculating the coefficients of the artificial criterion row, the $z' - c'$-row, may now be introduced. When there is a full artificial basis, as in this example, *all* basic variables in the initial tableau have c'-row coefficients of -1. Therefore the z'-row coefficient for any nonbasic variable is the sum of (each a_{ij} element in that nonbasic variable's column times -1), which simply equals minus the sum of the a_{ij} elements in that column. For instance, for the first column (x_1) of Tableau 1 in Table 14.1, the z'-row coefficient is $(1 \times -1) + (1 \times -1) + (7 \times -1)$, which may be expressed more simply as $-(1 + 1 + 7) = -9$.

Furthermore, since all nonbasic variables in the initial tableau have c'-row coefficients of zero, their z'-row and $z' - c'$-row elements are equal. Thus in the above example using the x_1 column, both z'-row and $z' - c'$-row coefficients are -9.

Hence for a problem with a full artificial basis we have the simple rule: The $z' - c'$-row element for the column of any nonbasic variable equals *minus the sum of the a_{ij} elements in that column*. To illustrate, let us apply this simple rule to some other columns in our initial tableau in Table 14.1. We find for x_2, for example, that the $z' - c'$-row element is simply

$$-(1 + 3 + 0) = -4$$

For s_3, for instance, the $z' - c'$-row element is:

$$-(0 + 0 + [-1]) = -[-1] = 1$$

For the b column the same rule holds; thus we obtain a $z' - c'$-row coefficient of

$$-(4 + 6 + 14) = -24$$

The reader may run through the full $z' - c'$-row calculations applied to this tableau to verify empirically for himself that the simple rule must always give the same answer as the long method of calculation.

14.2.2 Example 2

The illustration used in Chapter 10 was a problem of choosing a profit maximizing combination of cows (x_1) and pasture (x_2), subject to three maximum restrictions (on land, milking-shed capacity, and hay), one equality restriction (fertility), and two minimum restrictions (on land and fuel). Numerically the problem appears as follows:

Maximize

$$z = 40x_1 + 50x_2 \qquad (14.3a)$$

subject to

$$\tfrac{3}{5}x_1 + 1x_2 \leq 30 \text{ (maximum land)}$$
$$1x_1 \qquad\quad \leq 25 \text{ (maximum milking capacity)}$$
$$9x_1 - 15x_2 \leq 180 \text{ (maximum hay)}$$
$$1x_2 = 18 \text{ (fertility equality)} \qquad (14.3b)$$
$$\tfrac{3}{5}x_1 + 1x_2 \geq 6 \text{ (minimum land)}$$
$$14x_1 + 2x_2 \geq 84 \text{ (minimum fuel)}$$

and $$\qquad\qquad\qquad x_1, x_2 \geq 0 \qquad\qquad\qquad (14.3c)$$

Adding nonnegative slack, surplus, and artificial variables, we may write the set of constraint equations in full as

$$\tfrac{3}{5}x_1 + 1x_2 + 1s_1 \qquad\qquad\qquad\qquad\qquad\quad = 30$$
$$1x_1 \qquad\quad + 1s_2 \qquad\qquad\qquad\qquad\quad = 25$$
$$9x_1 - 15x_2 \qquad\quad + 1s_3 \qquad\qquad\qquad\quad = 180 \text{(14.4)}$$
$$1x_2 \qquad\qquad\qquad + 1s_4' \qquad\qquad = 18$$
$$\tfrac{3}{5}x_1 + 1x_2 \qquad\qquad - 1s_5 \qquad + 1s_5' \qquad = 6$$
$$14x_1 + 2x_2 \qquad\qquad\qquad - 1s_6 \qquad + 1s_6' = 84$$

in which s_1, s_2, s_3 are slack variables; s_5, s_6 are surplus variables; and s_4', s_5', s_6' are artificial variables.

Using the rules outlined above, we may check the construction of the $z - c$ row and the $z' - c'$ row of Tableau 1 for this problem.

Remember that here the c-row coefficients are profits and therefore positive. The $z - c$-row coefficients are the negatives of these values.

Moving to the artificial criterion row, we see that the c' row is written as usual. In calculating the z'-row coefficient for any column, we multiply each a_{ij} coefficient by the c-row coefficient of the corresponding basic variable. The six variables in the basis at Tableau 1 are the three maximum constraint slack activities, s_1, s_2, s_3, and the three artificial variables, s_4', s_5', s_6'. So we calculate the z'-row coefficient for the x_1 column, for example, as

0.6 acres slack land (s_1) × \$0 per acre	= \$0
1 head slack milking capacity (s_2) × \$0 per head	= \$0
9 cwt. slack hay (s_3) × \$0 per cwt.	= \$0
0 acres fertility equality artificial (s_4') × \$−1 per acre	= \$0
0.6 acres land minimum artificial (s_5') × \$−1 per acre	= \$−0.6
14 gals. fuel minimum artificial (s_6') × \$−1 per gallon	= \$−14.0
TOTAL	= \$−14.6

Hence introduction of cornmeal into the basis in Tableau 1 would "cost" \$14.6 per ton introduced, because of changes in the levels of currently basic variables.

Next the $z' - c'$-row coefficients are calculated in the usual way.

193

The simple rule derived in the previous section for computing the $z' - c'$-row coefficients more simply may be equally applied in this problem. In this case, however, there is not a full artificial basis; i.e., not all basic variables in the initial solution are artificial variables. Thus for any non-basic variable column, the $z' - c'$-row coefficient is calculated as: *minus the sum of the a_{ij} coefficients of that column in the rows of the basic ARTIFICIAL variables only.* This is because only the artificial variables have nonzero c'-row coefficients (the c'-row coefficients of basic *non-artificial* variables—e.g., the slack variables s_1, s_2, s_3 above—are always zero); hence only the artificial variables can contribute to z'. (Confirm this with the calculation of the z'-row coefficient for x_1 performed above.)

To illustrate, in Tableau 1 of the example in Chapter 10, the rows of the basic artificial variables, s'_4, s'_5, s'_6, are rows 4, 5, and 6 in the body of the tableau. Thus in calculating the $z' - c'$-row coefficients for this tableau, only the a_{ij} coefficients in these three rows are summed. For instance, the relevant elements in the x_2 column are 1, 1, and 2, hence the $z' - c'$-row coefficient of this column is calculated as: minus the sum of these three a_{ij} elements, i.e., as $-(1 + 1 + 2) = -4$. Similarly the $z' - c'$-row element in the b column of this tableau is equal to $-(18 + 6 + 84) = -108$.

The reader should check through the remaining coefficients of the z' row and $z' - c'$ rows to ensure that he fully understands the logic and mechanics of this calculation procedure.

14.3 Computation of Phase I

The aim of phase I is to maximize our artificial measure of profit by applying the ordinary simplex method to the problem, using the artificial criterion row as the means of selecting the variable to enter the basis at any iteration. Thus, as usual, we choose that activity with the highest negative $z' - c'$-row coefficient; if no negative $z' - c'$-row coefficients are present in the tableau, the basis contained therein is optimal. Let us follow through the computation of phase I for both examples.

14.3.1 Example 1

The largest negative value in the $z' - c'$-row of Tableau 1 of Table 14.1 belongs to the activity x_1 (cornmeal); this activity is therefore chosen to enter the basis. It will lead to an increase in profit of $9 per ton of cornmeal introduced.

By the usual technique the R column is calculated to determine which variable should leave the basis at iteration 1. We find that x_1 is permitted to increase to no more than 4 tons by the constraint imposed by variable s'_1, 6 tons by s'_2, and 2 tons by s'_3. We therefore conclude that the fiber

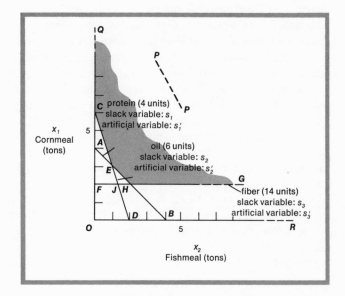

Figure 14.1

artificial variable s'_3 is the most limiting on the expansion of x_1, since it permits the smallest increase. Thus we choose s'_3 to leave the basis.

Iteration 1 is performed by applying the usual transformation rules. The reader should work through the calculations independently to verify the values of all coefficients in Tableau 2.

The procedure may be observed on the familiar two-dimensional graph of this problem shown in Figure 14.1. By selecting x_1 to enter the basis at iteration 1, we start the solution moving up the vertical axis away from its initial position at O. We can verify from the graph that the fiber constraint is indeed the first to be encountered, at point F, and that it does permit x_1 to expand to a level of 2 tons. (As an exercise the reader may verify the two other R-column values from the graph as well.) Besides containing x_1 at a level of 2 tons, the basis in Tableau 2 of Table 14.1 contains also the two artificial variables s'_1 and s'_2 at levels of 2 units protein and 4 units oil respectively, indicating that the solution is infeasible with respect to both the protein and the oil constraints. The reader may confirm graphically the values of these two variables, following the procedure outlined in section 6.3.

From the discussion in section 6.3 we can also understand that the value of the "artificial criterion" for any basis during phase I (i.e., the coefficient at the intersection of the b column and the $z' - c'$ row, measuring what we have been calling artificial profit) denotes in conglomerate units the aggregate "degree of infeasibility of the basis." But since this figure might be the sum of, say, acres, hundredweight, and tons all lumped

195

together, it clearly has no *numerical* significance. Its value is of relevance only insofar as whenever it is negative, the corresponding basis is infeasible with respect to at least one constraint in the problem.

The reader should himself check through iterations 2 and 3, leading successively to Tableaux 3 and 4 of Table 14.1, and verify the solutions obtained at each stage. He should observe that the Tableau 3 solution of $x_1 = 2$ tons, $x_2 = 1\frac{1}{3}$ tons, $s'_1 = \frac{2}{3}$ units, corresponds to point J in Figure 14.1, and that Tableau 4, in which the basis consists of $x_1 = 2$ tons, $x_2 = 2$ tons, $s_2 = 2$ units, represents point H. Note that as each artificial variable leaves the basis, its column is deleted from the tableau, since that variable can never be selected to reenter the solution and is therefore no longer of interest.

We observe that Tableau 4 is optimal with respect to the artificial criterion (no further negative elements in the $z' - c'$ row) and that the artificial criterion has reached its maximum value of zero. Phase I has therefore terminated in the finding of a first feasible basis, as contained in Tableau 4.

14.3.2   Example 2

The detailed computation of phase I of the example in Chapter 10 is left to the reader. It is suggested that he follow through this example carefully, and that he recheck the movement of the basis at each iteration against Figure 10.1, as was done in section 10.3.2.

14.4   Computation of Phase II

Little remains to round off the computational aspects of the two-phase simplex. We have seen that for any problem, phase I of this technique provides us with a tableau containing a *feasible* basis (if one exists) made up of real and/or slack and/or surplus variables, the artificial variables having disappeared altogether. This tableau may now be taken as the starting point for the "ordinary" simplex calculations.

It may be that the first feasible basis found from phase I is optimal with respect to total "real" profit or costs. This would be instantly recognized by the fact that its tableau would contain no negative elements in the $z - c$ row.

In neither of our numerical examples is the final tableau from phase I optimal. In the feed-mix example we see that Tableau 4 of Table 14.1 contains one negative element in its $z - c$ row, viz., $-\frac{2}{7}$ for the surplus variable s_3. This shows that for each unit of surplus fiber introduced into the solution (moving the basis from H up AB toward E in Figure 14.1), total costs of the feed mix will be reduced by $\$\frac{2}{7}$. (Strictly, since we are maximizing the negative of costs, we should state this as: " For each unit of s_3 introduced, the *negative* of total costs will be *increased* by $\$\frac{2}{7}$.") Thus we see that since 7 units of s_3 are introduced in the first iteration of phase II (moving the solution from Tableau 4 to Tableau 5) total costs are reduced by $\$(7 \times \frac{2}{7}) = \$2$; i.e., from $16 (Tableau 4) to $14 (Tableau 5). (In other words the *negative* of total costs is *increased* from $-16 to $-14.) Since no further negative $z - c$ elements exist in Tableau 5, the combination shown there of 3 tons of cornmeal and 1 ton of fishmeal, with 7 units of fiber surplus, is optimal. This feed mix leads to a minimum total cost of $14.

Similarly in example 2, the last matrix of phase I (Tableau 4) is not optimal, so the application of the ordinary simplex proceeds. Tableau 5 is reached, which contains the optimal solution. (Why is it optimal, even though there is a negative element in the $z - c$ row of Tableau 5? See section 10.3.2.)

Refer to Section 10.4. There three solution checks—a constraint check (10.4.1), a primal solution check (10.4.2), and a dual solution check (10.4.3)—were applied to example 2 above. It is left as a useful example for the reader to apply these same checks to the optimal tableau for example 1 above.

EXERCISES

1. Set up the initial tableau and calculate the artificial criterion row (i.e., the $z' - c'$ row) for each of the following problems:
   a. Chapter 6, exercise 3.
   b. Chapter 7, exercise 4.
   c. Chapter 8, exercise 1.
   d. Chapter 9, exercise 1(a).
   e. Chapter 9, exercise 1(b).
2. In the following problem, show that the initial basic feasible solution as determined by phase I of the simplex is also the optimum solution to the problem:

   Minimize
   $$z = 11x_1 + 8x_2$$
   subject to
   $$x_1 + x_2 \geq 5$$
   $$3x_1 + x_2 \geq 6$$
   and
   $$x_1, x_2 \geq 0$$

3. Use the simplex method to prove that no feasible solutions exist for the problems in parts (d) and (e) of exercise 1.

4. Find a feasible solution to the set of constraints in part (c) of exercise 1, using phase I of the simplex.

5. Prove by means of the simplex that there exists only one set of values of x_1 and x_2 which satisfies the following constraints:

$$3x_1 + x_2 \leq 12$$
$$x_1 + 2x_2 \leq 8$$
$$x_1 + x_2 \geq 18\tfrac{}{5}$$

6. Find the optimum solution to the problem in part (a) of exercise 1, using the two-phase simplex method. Trace the solution path on a graph of the constraint set for this problem.

7. Use the two-phase simplex method to solve the problem in part (b) of exercise 1.

15

SUMMARY OF
THE COMPLETE SIMPLEX

In this chapter we summarize in easily accessible form *all* the rules of the simplex. The rules are presented in a concise *general* manner; i.e., they are written in a form equally applicable to phases I and II of the two-phase simplex. The only difference between the two phases is that each uses its own criterion row for selection of the introduced variable and for testing for optimality. A new example is worked through in this chapter as a summary illustration of the application of these calculation methods. The example also provides the reader with an opportunity to practice many of the techniques learnt in previous chapters.

15.1 An Example:
The Airlift Problem

15.1.1 Description

An embattled city completely surrounded by enemy territory is cut off without food. An airlift is therefore organized which can make use of two types of aircraft. Type 1 has a capacity for 125 tons of food, of which up to 20 tons can be refrigerated cargo; type 2 can carry a payload of 200 tons, but does not have a refrigerating section. The runway in the besieged city's airfield can handle no more than 25 flights of either type of aircraft a day; but an extra runway under the control of the enemy may be used, provided that for every flight using this runway a fee of 50 tons of food is paid to the enemy authorities immediately on landing. Although aircraft for the operation are in unlimited supply, personnel for loading and flying them is not. There are 120 loading men and 220 aircrew at the air base from which the operation is being mounted, and it is known that a type 1 aircraft requires

5 aircrew and 8 loading crew per flight, while type 2 needs 6 aircrew and 4 loaders. Each pilot and each loader can work on only one flight each day.

The officer in charge of planning the airlift, realizing that loaders are in short supply, permits a pilot to become a loader if necessary (but not vice versa). The loaders union representative agrees to this arrangement, provided that the total number of the aircrew transferred to loader's duties does not exceed twice the number of regular loaders actually employed on flights (as distinct from twice the number of loaders *available*, i.e., 2×120). When a pilot becomes a loader, he is no longer available for aircrew duties.

Finally, one condition of the airlift is that at least 110 tons of refrigerated cargo be carried each day.

The objective of the planner is to determine the number of flights by each type of aircraft which will maximize the amount of food flown to the city each day. An essential aspect of the problem is the assignment of the aircrew and the loaders to their tasks and the determination of how many (if any) of the aircrew should transfer to loading duties. A further problem to be solved is the optimum use (if any) to be made of the enemy's offer (at a price) of extra runway space.

15.1.2 Setting up the Problem

Although, at first glance, the previous paragraph might suggest that several distinct optimizations are involved, the overall question is easily reducible to a single optimization, amenable to solution by linear programming. Before proceeding, the reader may attempt by himself to set up the problem in these terms.

The initial task is to define the decision variables involved, i.e., those variables whose levels the decision maker is setting out to determine. Clearly two decision variables will be the number of flights per day for each of the two types of aircraft. Let us denote the number of flights per day by aircraft type 1 as x_1 and by aircraft type 2 as x_2.

We know the amounts of food carried per flight by each aircraft type. Then if our objective is to maximize the amount of food flown in each day, the problem may be initially written down as:

Maximize

$$z = 125x_1 + 200x_2 \tag{15.1}$$

Disregarding for the time being questions of crew transfer and of hiring extra runways, we can immediately write constraints on the levels of x_1 and x_2 imposed by the availability of aircrew, loading crew, and runway capacity, as follows:

$$
\begin{aligned}
5x_1 + 6x_2 &\leq 220 \quad \text{(aircrew: number of men)} \\
8x_1 + 4x_2 &\leq 120 \quad \text{(loading crew: number of men)} \\
1x_1 + 1x_2 &\leq 25 \quad \text{(runway capacity: number of flights)}
\end{aligned}
\tag{15.2}
$$

These are, of course, simple maximum constraints specifying that the total number of aircrew, the total number of loading crew, and the total number of flights should not exceed available supplies of aircrew, loading crew, and runway capacity respectively.

Now we know that the number of loading crew may be supplemented if necessary, so let us define another variable—x_3, transfer pilots to loaders—measured in terms of numbers of men transferred. Thus whenever x_3 appears in a given solution, its value will indicate how many pilots should be transferred to loaders in that solution. The level of x_3 will have no *direct* influence on the amount of food carried, so its contribution to the objective function of equation (15.1) is nil, i.e., that equation now becomes

$$z = 125x_1 + 200x_2 + 0x_3 \qquad (15.3)$$

The variable x_3 will *indirectly* permit increases in food shipments, because it will allow bottlenecks in loader supply to be broken. How? For every unit of x_3 in a solution, one pilot is "used up" from the aircrew constraint and "supplied" to the loading crew constraint. Thus we now write these two constraints as

$$\begin{aligned} 5x_1 + 6x_2 + 1x_3 &\le 220 \\ 8x_1 + 4x_2 - 1x_3 &\le 120 \end{aligned} \qquad (15.4)$$

showing that, in the first constraint, every unit of x_3 competes with x_1 and x_2 for the available supply of 220 aircrew; i.e., each of the activities x_1, x_2, x_3 "absorbs" pilots, and hence each has a positive coefficient in this maximum constraint (see section 8.4). Similarly in the second constraint of (15.4), each unit of x_3 "donates" a man (having a negative coefficient, following again the logic of section 8.4). In this constraint, the total number of men supplied by this activity (i.e., $1 \times x_3$) is added to the 120-man supply, in satisfying the needs of x_1 and x_2 for loading crew.

Furthermore, mindful of the loaders union representative, we must add a constraint on x_3 to indicate that it should be no greater than twice the number of loaders used by x_1 and x_2, as shown in inequation (15.5):

$$x_3 \le 2(8x_1 + 4x_2) \qquad (15.5)$$

This constraint reads: The number of men transferred to pilots duties (x_3) must be equal to or less than twice (the total number of loaders used by x_1 [i.e., $8 \times x_1$] *plus* the total used by x_2 [i.e., $4 \times x_2$]). Hence we obtain directly

$$-16x_1 - 8x_2 + 1x_3 \le 0 \qquad (15.6)$$

which may be added to our existing set of constraints.

Next we must account for the possibility of hiring extra runway capacity from the enemy. Let us define a variable x_4 as the number of flights per day to be operated on the enemy's runway. Then it is clear that the runway capacity constraint in (15.2) must be augmented by this supply; i.e., the number of flights possible per day is now 25 *plus* this new variable x_4. In other words this constraint should be rewritten as

$$1x_1 + 1x_2 \le 25 + 1x_4 \tag{15.7}$$

which is equivalently expressed as

$$1x_1 + 1x_2 - 1x_4 \le 25 \tag{15.8}$$

in which we again see positive and negative signs performing their appropriate functions for a maximum constraint.

This variable x_4 *does* have a direct effect on the amount of food reaching the starving inhabitants, since for each unit (i.e., flight) of x_4, 50 tons of food are lost in fees. In other words every unit of x_4 *subtracts* 50 tons out of the equation expressing total amount of food delivered. Thus equation (15.3) becomes

$$z = 125x_1 + 200x_2 + 0x_3 - 50x_4 \tag{15.9}$$

It might be thought that in choosing values of the x variables to maximize equation (15.9) we could never select x_4, since each unit introduced would *reduce* total food delivered (z in equation [15.9]). However this is not so; x_4 could be selected because it can allow, through constraint (15.8), the values of x_1 and/or x_2 to be increased. The gains from this may well outweigh the 50 tons of food lost per unit of x_4; whether or not this will occur will be seen during the solution to the problem.

Finally a minimum constraint on refrigerated food must be added. This is simply expressed as follows:

$$20x_1 \ge 110 \tag{15.10}$$

So the complete problem may be written as follows:

Maximize

$$z = 125x_1 + 200x_2 + 0x_3 - 50x_4 \tag{15.11a}$$

subject to

$$\begin{array}{llll}
5x_1 + 6x_2 + 1x_3 & \le 220 & \text{(aircrew: men)} & \\
8x_1 + 4x_2 - 1x_3 & \le 120 & \text{(loaders: men)} & \\
1x_1 + 1x_2 \quad - 1x_4 & \le \; 25 & \text{(runway capacity: flights)} & (15.11b) \\
-16x_1 + 8x_2 + 1x_3 & \le \;\; 0 & \text{(transfer restriction: men)} & \\
20x_1 & \ge 110 & \text{(refrigerated cargo: tons)} &
\end{array}$$

and

$$x_1, \cdots, x_4 \ge 0 \tag{15.11c}$$

Let us next define slack variables s_1 to s_4 corresponding to the four maximum constraints in (15.11b), and a surplus variable s_5 to attach to the minimum constraint. An artificial variable, s_5', must also be added to this minimum constraint to complete an initial basis.

To complete the setting up of this problem, we may construct the initial tableau. It is shown in Table 15.1.

15.2 Summary of the Rules

The sequence of operations for the complete solution of a linear programming problem by the simplex procedure is summarized in Figure 15.1. Rules 1 through 5 mentioned in that figure are summarized below. In section 15.3 the application of these operations to the above airlift problem will be illustrated.

Rule 1

Rules 1A, 1B and 1C involve the derivation of the c, z, and $z - c$ rows (and the c', z', and $z' - c'$ rows during phase I of the two-phase simplex). These three rules are by-passed by the direct calculation of the $z - c$ row (and the $z' - c'$ row in phase I). The procedure adopted depends upon whether it is the initial tableau or any subsequent tableau under consideration:

Initial Tableau

$z - c$ row	$z' - c'$ row (if artificial variables are present)

a. Columns of the nonbasic variables

Each $z - c$-*row coefficient is taken directly from the original objective function.* If the problem is one of maximization, the signs of the coefficients are changed. Thus according to our convention, whether the original problem is one of maximization or of minimization, *in the* z-c *row net profits are negative and net costs are positive.*	*Each* $z' - c'$-*row coefficient is calculated as the negative sum of the* a_{ij} *elements in the column of the nonbasic variables in rows corresponding only to artificial variables in the initial basis.*

b. Columns of the basic variables

$z - c$-row coefficients are zero.	$z' - c'$-row coefficients are zero.

c. b column

$z - c$-row coefficient is normally zero.	$z' - c'$-row coefficient is calculated in the same way as for the nonbasic variables.

Any Subsequent Tableau

The $z - c$ *and* $z' - c'$ *rows will be calculated during the transformation of the main tableau* (rule 5).

TABLE 15.1

| | Real Variables | | | | Surplus Variable | Slack Variables | | | | Artificial Variable | | |
	Aircraft Type 1 (flights) x_1	Aircraft Type 2 (flights) x_2	Crew Transfer (men) x_3	Runway Hire (flights) x_4	Refrigerated Cargo (tons) s_5	Aircrew (men) s_1	Load Crew (men) s_2	Runway Capacity (flights) s_3	Transfer Restriction (men) s_4	Refrigerated Cargo s_5'	b	Basic Variables
	-125	-200	0	50	0	0	0	0	0	0	0	$z - c$ row
	5	6	1	0	0	1	0	0	0	0	220	s_1 Slack aircrew
	8	4	-1	0	0	0	1	0	0	0	120	s_2 Slack loaders
	1	1	0	-1	0	0	0	1	0	0	25	s_3 Slack runway
	-16	-8	1	0	0	0	0	0	1	0	0	s_4 Slack transfer
	20	0	0	0	-1	0	0	0	0	1	110	s_5' Artificial (refrigerated cargo)
	-20	0	0	0	1	0	0	0	0	0	-110	$z' - c'$ row

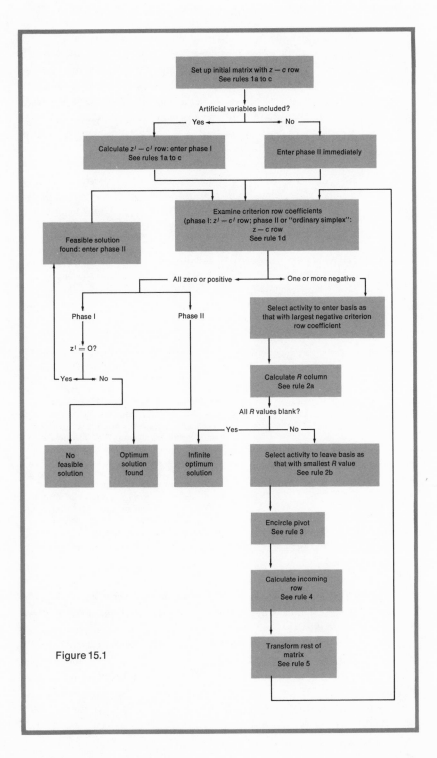

Figure 15.1

Rule 1D incorporates the optimality test and the procedure for selection of the introduced variable. During phase I of the two-phase simplex, the criterion row used is the $z' - c'$ row. During phase II (or during the "ordinary" simplex without artificial variables), the criterion row is the $z - c$ row. *Examine the criterion-row coefficients of all nonbasic variables* (in phase II of the two-phase simplex, disregard any nonbasic artificial variables). Either there will be one or more criterion-row coefficients negative, or all coefficients will be zero or positive:

a. If one or more coefficients are negative: the basis is not optimal with respect to the relevant criterion. Therefore, *select as the activity to enter the basis the nonbasic variable with the largest negative coefficient in the relevant criterion row.* Mark the position of this "introduced activity" column on the tableau with a vertical arrow, and proceed to rule 2.

b. If all coefficients are zero or positive: no activity can be introduced into the basis which will improve the value of the criterion. The basis contained in this matrix is therefore optimal with respect to the given criterion. The next move depends on whether the $z - c$ row or the $z' - c'$ row is the current criterion row (i.e., whether we are in phase II ["ordinary" simplex] or phase I):

$z - c$ row	$z' - c'$ row
The required optimal solution has been found.	a. *If the optimal value of the artificial criterion is zero,* then all artificial variables are zero, the basis is feasible and *phase II may be initiated by restarting from the beginning of rule 1D,* now using the $z - c$ row as the criterion row. b. *If the optimal value of the artificial criterion is less than zero,* then one or more artificial variables remain in the basis at a nonzero level. This combination of real and/or slack and/or surplus variables is therefore infeasible, and *no feasible solution to the problem exists.*

Rule 2

Rule 2A. Calculate the R column by *dividing each matrix element (a_{ij} coefficient) in the column of the introduced variable into the corresponding element in the b column.*

If any a_{ij} coefficient is zero or negative, the corresponding basic activity does not constrain the introduced variable. This basic activity may therefore be excluded from consideration by leaving a blank for its R-column value.

If any b-column entry of zero is divided by a positive a_{ij} coefficient, the corresponding R value is zero.

Rule 2B. Examine all coefficients in the R *column, including zeros but disregarding blanks. Select, as the activity to leave the basis, that with the smallest* R *value.* Mark its position on the tableau with a horizontal arrow.

If the R column is completely blank (i.e., if all a_{ij} coefficients in the introduced variable column are either negative or zero), then the introduced variable may enter the basis at infinite level and the optimal solution to the problem is infinite.

If two or more basic activities "tie" for the smallest R value, choose as the variable to leave the basis that which is closest to the top of the tableau. This is an arbitrary procedure which always works.

Rule 3

The coefficient at the intersection of the introduced variable column and the eliminated variable row in the "old tableau"—i.e., the tableau awaiting transformation to which rules 1 and 2 have just been applied—is called the "pivot." Encircle it.

Rule 4

The elements of the incoming row are calculated by dividing each coefficient in the eliminated variable row in the old tableau by the pivot. The "incoming row" thus derived should be written in the new tableau in the same position as the eliminated variable row in the old tableau.

Rule 5

This rule embodies the main calculations for transformation of the matrix elements to complete one iteration.

On a separate worksheet write the coefficients of the outgoing column of the old tableau, including the $z - c$-row coefficient (and the $z' - c'$-row coefficient if in phase I). Write also the coefficients of the incoming row of the new tableau, including the b-column coefficient.

From the coefficient at the intersection of the ith *row and* jth *column of the old tableau is subtracted the product of the* ith *-row coefficient and the* jth *column coefficient in the incoming row. This will give a new coefficient which will be written at the intersection of the* ith *row and the* jth *column of the new tableau.*

This rule is applied to all coefficients in the old tableau except those of the eliminated variable row which have already been transformed into the coefficients of the new incoming row. In other words, with this one exception, all a_{ij}, b, $z - c$ (and $z' - c'$ in phase I) coefficients are transformed by use of this rule.

When these calculations are finished, the complete new tableau is formed, and we *return to rule 1D*.

15.3 Application of the
Simplex Rules to the Airlift Problem

We shall now illustrate the complete simplex rules summarized in section 15.2 by observing their application to the airlift problem which was set up in section 15.1. The complete set of matrixes obtained during the solution of this problem is shown in Table 15.2. The reader may work through each iteration with the aid of the brief commentary below.

Iteration 1

Rules 1A, 1B and 1C. In the original objective function (15.11a), two activities, x_1 and x_2, have nonzero profits, while one activity, x_4, carries a nonzero cost. Thus in transferring these coefficients directly to the $z - c$ row of Tableau 1 in Table 15.2, we write the profit coefficients as negative, viz., -125 and -200 in columns 1 and 2, and the cost coefficients as positive, viz., $+50$ in column 4.

There is only one artificial activity, s_5', in the initial basis; hence in calculating the $z' - c'$ row for Tableau 1 in Table 15.2, we need consider only one row of the matrix, viz., the last row in the body of the tableau. Thus the $z' - c'$-row element for the x_1 column, for example, is the negative sum of just one coefficient, the element 20 in the s_5' row. Similarly the b-column element is calculated as -110.

Rule 1D. Since at this stage we are in phase I of the two-phase simplex, the criterion row in Tableau 1 to which we apply rule 1D is the $z' - c'$ row. Negative elements are present in this criterion row, hence the basis is not optimal with respect to the artificial criterion. Thus, in terms of part b of rule 1D, we select activity x_1, aircraft type 1, to enter the basis at this iteration, since it has the largest negative $z' - c'$-row coefficient, -20.

Rule 2. The R column, reading downward, is calculated as follows:

b-column Value	÷	a_{ij} Value in Introduced Variable Column	=	R Value
220	÷	5	=	44
120	÷	8	=	15
25	÷	1	=	25
0	÷	-16	=	— (blank)
110	÷	20	=	5.5 ←

It is clear that the coefficient 5.5 is the smallest value in this column; the basic variable corresponding to this value is the artificial variable s_5', and hence it is chosen to leave the basis.

TABLE 15.2
Tableau 1

	(1)	(2)	(3)	(4)	(5)	(6)	(7)	(8)	(9)	(10)	(11)		
	x_1	x_2	x_3	x_4	s_5	s_1	s_2	s_3	s_4	s_5'	b		R
(1)	-125	-200	0	50	0	0	0	0	0	0	0	$z - c$ row	0
												Basic Variables	
(2)	5	6	1	0	0	1	0	0	0	0	220	s_1 Slack aircrew	44
(3)	8	4	-1	0	0	0	1	0	0	0	120	s_2 Slack loaders	15
(4)	1	1	0	-1	0	0	0	1	0	0	25	s_3 Slack runway	25
(5)	-16	-8	1	0	0	0	0	0	1	0	0	s_4 Slack transfer	—
(6)	⑳	0	0	0	-1	0	0	0	0	1	110	s_5' Artificial (refrigerated cargo)	5.5 ←
(7)	-20	0	0	0	0	0	0	0	0	0	-110	$z' - c'$ row	0

↑

Tableau 2

	x_1	x_2	x_3	x_4	s_5	s_1	s_2	s_3	s_4	s_5'	b	$z-c$ row		R
(1)	0	−200	0	50	−6.25	0	0	0	0	6.25	687.5	$z-c$ row	Basic Variables	
(2)	0	6	1	0	0.25	1	0	0	0	−0.25	192.5		s_1 Slack aircrew	32.083
(3)	0	④	−1	−1	0.4	0	1	0	0	−0.4	76		s_2 Slack loaders	19 ←
(4)	0	1	0	0	0.05	0	0	1	0	−0.05	19.5		s_3 Slack runway	19.5
(5)	0	−8	1	0	−0.8	0	0	0	1	0.8	88		s_4 Slack transfer	—
(6)	1	0	0	0	−0.05	0	0	0	0	0.05	5.5		x_1 Type 1 aircraft	—
(7)	0	0	0	0	0	0	0	0	0	1	0	$z'-c'$ row		

Tableau 3

	x_1	x_2	x_3	x_4	s_5	s_1	s_2	s_3	s_4	s_5'	b	$z-c$ row		R
(1)	0	0	−50	50	13.75	0	50	0	0	−13.75	4,487.5	$z-c$ row	Basic Variables	
(2)	0	0	2.5	0	−0.35	1	−1.5	0	0		78.5		s_1 Slack aircrew	31.4
(3)	0	1	−0.25	0	0.1	0	0.25	0	0		19		x_2 Type 2 aircraft	—
(4)	0	0	⓪.25	−1	−0.05	0	−0.25	1	0		0.5		s_3 Slack runway	2 ←
(5)	0	0	−1	0	0	0	2	0	1		240		s_4 Slack transfer	—
(6)	1	0	0	0	−0.05	0	0	0	0		5.5		x_1 Type 1 aircraft	—

Tableau 4

	x_1	x_2	x_3	x_4	s_5	s_1	s_2	s_3	s_4	s_5'	b	$z - c$ row	R
(1)	0	0	0	−150	3.75	0	0	200	0	−3.75	4,587.5		
												Basic Variables	
(2)	0	0	0	⑩	0.15	1	1	−10	0		73.5	s_1 Slack aircrew	7.35←
(3)	0	1	0	−1	0.05	0	0	1	0		19.5	x_2 Type 2 aircraft	—
(4)	0	0	1	−4	−0.2	0	−1	4	0		2	x_3 Crew transfer	—
(5)	0	0	0	−4	−0.2	0	1	4	1		24.2	s_4 Slack transfer	—
(6)	1	0	0	0	−0.05	0	0	0	0		5.5	x_1 Type 1 aircraft	—

Tableau 5

	x_1	x_2	x_3	x_4	s_5	s_1	s_2	s_3	s_4	s_5'	b	$z - c$ row
(1)	0	0	0	0	6	15	15	50	0	−6	5,690	
												Basic Variables
(2)	0	0	0	1	0.015	0.1	0.1	−1	0		7.35	x_4 Runway hire
(3)	0	1	0	0	0.065	0.1	0.1	0	0		26.85	x_2 Type 2 aircraft
(4)	0	0	1	0	−0.14	0.4	−0.6	0	0		31.4	x_3 Crew transfer
(5)	0	0	0	0	−0.14	0.4	1.4	0	1		271.4	s_4 Slack transfer
(6)	1	0	0	0	−0.05	0	0	0	0		5.5	x_1 Type 1 aircraft

Rule 3. With x_1 chosen as the introduced variable for iteration 1 and s_5' chosen as the eliminated variable, we locate the pivot, the coefficient 20, and encircle it as shown on Tableau 1 of Table 15.2.

Rule 4. The incoming row at iteration 1 is calculated by dividing each element in the s_5' row of Tableau 1 by 20. Thus, working from left to right we get

Eliminated Variable Row in Tableau 1	$\div$	Pivot	$=$	Incoming Row in Tableau 2
20	$\div$	20	$=$	1
0	$\div$	20	$=$	0
0	$\div$	20	$=$	0
0	$\div$	20	$=$	0
-1	$\div$	20	$=$	-0.05
0	$\div$	20	$=$	0
0	$\div$	20	$=$	0
0	$\div$	20	$=$	0
1	$\div$	20	$=$	0.05
110	$\div$	20	$=$	5.5

This new row is written in Tableau 2 in the same position as the eliminated variable row occupied in Tableau 1, i.e., the last row in the body of the matrix.

At this point also the name of the new basic variable may be written in the identification column at the right-hand side of the matrix. Thus opposite the incoming row in Tableau 2 we write the identification " type 1 aircraft "; the identifications attaching to all other rows in Tableau 2, of course, remain the same as they were in the previous tableau.

Rule 5. First let us define i and j. We shall refer to the $z - c$ row of any tableau in the airlift problem as row 1, then let us assign the numbers 2 to 6 to the five constraint rows, finally referring to the $z' - c'$ row as row 7. This set of numbers constitutes the row index, i. Likewise let us assign values to the column index j. We shall assign the numbers 1 through 11 to the columns in Table 15.2, going from left to right; the last of these numbers, 11, is attached to the b column.

Next to the outgoing column at iteration 1, the x_1 column in Tableau 1 of Table 15.2 is written as

Row Number (i) in Tableau

-125	1
5	2
8	3
1	4
-16	5
20	6
-20	7

Similarly the incoming row (the x_1 row of Tableau 2) is written as

| 1 | 0 | 0 | 0 | -0.05 | 0 | 0 | 0 | 0 | 0.05 | 5.5 |

Column Number
(j) in Tableau   1   2   3   4   5   6   7   8   9   10   11

Now the calculations, working across each row, proceed as follows:

Row	Column	Coefficient in Old Tableau	−	Outgoing Column Element	×	Incoming Row Element	=	Coefficient in New Tableau
1	1	-125	−	$(-125$	×	1)	=	0
	2	-200	−	$(-125$	×	0)	=	-200
	3	0	−	$(-125$	×	0)	=	0
	4	50	−	$(-125$	×	0)	=	50
	5	0	−	$(-125$	×	$-0.05)$	=	-6.25
	6	0	−	$(-125$	×	0)	=	0
	7	0	−	$(-125$	×	0)	=	0
	8	0	−	$(-125$	×	0)	=	0
	9	0	−	$(-125$	×	0)	=	0
	10	0	−	$(-125$	×	0.05)	=	6.25
	11	0	−	$(-125$	×	5.5)	=	687.5
2	1	5	−	(5	×	1)	=	0
	2	6	−	(5	×	0)	=	6
	3	1	−	(5	×	0)	=	1
	4	0	−	(5	×	0)	=	0
	5	0	−	(5	×	$-0.05)$	=	0.25
	6	1	−	(5	×	0)	=	1
	7	0	−	(5	×	0)	=	0
	8	0	−	(5	×	0)	=	0
	9	0	−	(5	×	0)	=	0
	10	0	−	(5	×	0.05)	=	-0.25
	11	220	−	(5	×	5.5)	=	192.5
3	1	8	−	(8	×	1)	=	0
	2	4	−	(8	×	0)	=	4
	3	-1	−	(8	×	0)	=	-1
·	·	·	·	·	·	·	·	·
·	·	·	·	·	·	·	·	·
·	·	·	·	·	·	·	·	·
5	8	0	−	$(-16$	×	0)	=	0
	9	1	−	$(-16$	×	0)	=	1
	10	0	−	$(-16$	×	0.05)	=	0.8
	11	0	−	$(-16$	×	5.5)	=	88.0
6	(Incoming row already calculated)							
7	1	-20	−	$(-20$	×	1)	=	0
	2	0	−	$(-20$	×	0)	=	0
	3	0	−	$(-20$	×	0)	=	0
	4	0	−	$(-20$	×	0)	=	0
	5	1	−	$(-20$	×	$-0.05)$	=	0
·	·	·	·	·	·	·	·	·
·	·	·	·	·	·	·	·	·
·	·	·	·	·	·	·	·	·
	9	0	−	$(-20$	×	0)	=	0
	10	0	−	$(-20$	×	0.05)	=	1
	11	-110	−	$(-20$	×	5.5)	=	0

Rule 1D. All coefficients in the artificial criterion row in Tableau 2 of Table 15.2 are zero or positive. Furthermore the value of z', at the intersection of the b column and the $z' - c'$ row, is zero. Hence the current basis is feasible.

Thus phase II is initiated by discarding the $z' - c'$ row and henceforth using the $z - c$ row as the criterion row. We start the second iteration by reapplying rule 1D.

Iteration 2

Rule 1D. The $z - c$ row in Tableau 2 of Table 15.2 contains some negative elements, hence the current basis is not optimal. We select x_2, with a $z - c$-row coefficient of -200, as the nonbasic activity to enter the basis at this iteration. Its column is marked with a vertical arrow, as shown in Table 15.2.

Rule 2. The R column, reading downward, is calculated as follows for this iteration:

b-column Value	$\div$	a_{ij} Value in Introduced Variable Column	$=$	R Value
192.5	$\div$	6	$=$	32.08
76.0	$\div$	4	$=$	19.00$\leftarrow$
19.5	$\div$	1	$=$	19.50
88.0	$\div$	-8	$=$	— (blank)
5.5	$\div$	0	$=$	— (blank)

The smallest R value, 19.00, corresponds to the variable s_2, slack loading crew. This activity is thus selected to leave the basis at this iteration.

Rule 3. With "type 2 aircraft" replacing "slack loading crew" at this iteration, the pivot is the coefficient 4 lying at the intersection of the x_2 column and the s_2 row.

Rule 4. The eliminated variable row in Tableau 2 of Table 15.2 is the second row in the body of the matrix, hence the incoming row at this iteration is written as the second in the body of Tableau 3. Its coefficients, working from left to right, are calculated as follows:

Eliminated Variable Row in Tableau 2	$\div$	Pivot	$=$	Incoming Row in Tableau 3
0	$\div$	4	$=$	0
4	$\div$	4	$=$	1
-1	$\div$	4	$=$	-0.25
0	$\div$	4	$=$	0
0.4	$\div$	4	$=$	0.1
0	$\div$	4	$=$	0
1	$\div$	4	$=$	0.25
0	$\div$	4	$=$	0
0	$\div$	4	$=$	0
-0.4	$\div$	4	$=$	-0.1
76.0	$\div$	4	$=$	19.0

The name of the new basic variable, "type 2 aircraft," is substituted for that of the eliminated variable, "slack-loading crew," in the list of basic variables at the right-hand side of Tableau 3 in Table 15.2.

Rule 5.   The application of this rule proceeds as before and it is left as an exercise for the reader to work through its detailed mechanics at this and subsequent iterations.

Iterations 3 and 4

Let us briefly check through the sequence of solutions to the optimum in Table 15.2.

Tableau 3 contains a plan involving 5.5 flights of type 1 aircraft (just satisfying the refrigerated cargo restriction, since 5.5 flights *times* 20 tons per flight *equals* 110 tons of refrigerated food) and 19 flights of type 2 aircraft. This plan transports a total of 4,487.5 tons of food per day. This plan just uses up all the loading crew, since (5.5 type 1 flights *times* 8 loaders per flight) *plus* (19 type 2 flights *times* 4 loaders per flight) *equals* 120 loaders. Will it pay to transfer aircrew to loading duties? The $z - c$ row of Tableau 3 shows that each man transferred (i.e., each unit of x_3 introduced into the basis) would cause a *net increase* of 50 tons of food shipped ($z - c$-row coefficient $= -50$). This is the largest possible increase available at this iteration (i.e., the largest negative $z - c$-row coefficient belongs to x_3), hence we select x_3 to enter the basis in accordance with rule 1D. The R column of Tableau 3 shows that 31.4 men could be transferred before we would run out of slack aircrew; but, well before this stage could be reached, runway capacity would be exhausted, since the variable s_3 permits an increase of only two men in x_3. Thus s_3, being the activity most limiting the introduced variable x_3, is chosen to leave the basis at iteration 3.

The solution found in Tableau 4 is not yet optimal, since a net increase in food transported of 150 tons can still be achieved for each flight introduced into the basis, using the enemy's runway facilities. Note that the absolute value of the $z - c$-row coefficient for x_4 in Tableau 4 is simply the amount of food carried on each type 2 aircraft (200 tons) less the fee of 50 tons per flight. Introduction of x_4 enables us to use up all the rest of the idle aircrew as loaders by eliminating s_1 (slack aircrew) from the plan.

The optimal plan, shown in Tableau 5 of Table 15.2, specifies that the maximum amount of food which can be shipped to the town per day is 5,690 tons, using 5.5 flights of aircraft type 1 and 26.85 flights of aircraft type 2, transferring 31.4 aircrew to loaders, and running 7.35 flights through the enemy runway. We see that the loaders union representative need not have worried. The 271.4 units of the slack variable s_4 in the optimal solution show that this crew transfer constraint comes nowhere near to limiting the decision variables in this problem.

Note that in interpreting this solution for real-world action, figures would need to be rounded off to the nearest whole number, since fractions of a flight are not possible. Thus, the optimal solution would have to be expressed as *6* flights of aircraft type 1 and *27* flights of type 2. Rounding solutions to integer values in this way may, in some cases, introduce important problems, which need not concern us at this stage.

The detailed primal solution and constraint checks are left to the reader, who should follow through the computational method and logical interpretation set out in sections 10.4.1 and 10.4.2. The dual solution check is referred to below.

15.4   Dual Solution Check in Problems with Mixed Constraints

Some difficulties of interpretation may arise in performing the dual solution check on simplex tableaux for problems containing more than one type of constraint. One example of this has already been encountered in Chapter 10, where the allocation problem contained maximum, minimum, and equality constraints. Another example is the airlift problem above; let us use its optimal tableau as a basis for discussion.

The shadow "prices" for variables s_1 (slack aircrew) and s_5 (surplus refrigerated cargo) are 15 tons of food per man and 6 tons of food per ton of refrigerated cargo respectively, read from the $z - c$ row of Tableau 5 of Table 15.2. Both variables are nonbasic and have nonzero shadow prices, hence the corresponding original constraints (the first and the fifth in Tableau 1) are "effective" or "fully met" in the final solution. But s_1 is a slack variable and s_5 is a surplus variable, being attached originally to a maximum and a minimum constraint respectively. Hence increasing the supply of aircrew by 1 man would permit an extra 15 tons of food to be flown in each day, whereas an increase in the requirement for refrigerated cargo of 1 ton would *reduce* the total quantity of food shipped by 6 tons.

This explanation helps make sense of the dual solution check, which according to the usual rules proceeds as shown in Table 15.3. It is convenient to conceptualize the "contribution" of this refrigerated cargo

TABLE 15.3

$z - c$-row Value of Nonbasic Variable	$\times$	Original b-Column Coefficient	$=$	Total Cost (tons)
6 tons per ton surplus refrigerated cargo	$\times$	0 tons	$=$	0
15 tons per man slack aircrew	$\times$	220 men	$=$	3,300
15 tons per man slack loaders	$\times$	120 men	$=$	1,800
50 tons per flight slack runway	$\times$	25 flights	$=$	1,250
-6 tons per ton artificial refrigerated cargo	$\times$	110 tons	$=$	-660
		TOTAL	$=$	5,690

requirement to total food shipped in one of two ways: as the shadow price of the surplus variable s_5 *times* its actual value at the initial solution (i.e., $6 \times -110 = -660$ tons of food), or as the shadow price of the artificial variable s_5' *times* its level in the initial basis (i.e., $-6 \times 110 = -660$ tons of food). The latter is the direct interpretation, which appears in Table 15.3.

EXERCISES

1. A wholesale cigarette distributor supplies three retail outlets, A, B, and C, from two warehouses, X and Y. The weekly demands at the three outlets are 200,000, 300,000, and 150,000 cartons respectively and the capacities of the two warehouses are 250,000 and 400,000 cartons respectively. The transport costs in dollars per thousand cartons from each warehouse to each destination are as follows:

	Outlet		
Warehouse	A	B	C
X	5	2	1
Y	3	5	4

Using straightforward linear programming, find the distribution from each warehouse to each outlet which minimizes the distributor's weekly costs of transportation. Assume that delivery takes place on Monday morning from the warehouses, which have been filled to capacity at the weekend. No shortages are allowed at the demand points, and the warehouses must be empty at the end of delivery.

2. A sharecropper is offered areas on four farms for the coming season. Farm A will allow him up to 20 acres, farm B up to 10 acres, farm C up to 40 acres, and farm D up to 70 acres. His labor input over the season in growing crops on farms A, B, C, and D will be 5, 2, 6, and 1 hours per acre respectively, while his net profits will be $60, $30, $55, and $15 per acre respectively. What combination of areas will enable the sharecropper to maximize his leisure time, given that he requires a minimum net income of (a) $2,500? (b) $4,000?

3. A mythical economy consists of three sectors, a primary sector (P), a transport sector (T), and an industrial sector (I), whose outputs are measured in convenient units (e.g., dollars). The following relationships describe the workings of this economy:
   a. T and I require food produced by P. Each unit of output of P yields 10 units of food, T and I requiring 25 and 20 units of food respectively to produce 1 unit of output. A stockpile of 500 units of food is on hand at the start of the base period under study.

217

b. P and I use 1 and 2 units of T's services respectively per unit of output.

c. I uses 1 unit of a particular raw material per unit of output, which is supplied by P at the rate of 1 unit per unit of P's output.

d. A labor force of 1,000 men is available, which finds employment in P, T, and I at the rate of 15, 5, and 10 men per unit of respective outputs.

What levels of output of all three sectors will enable the output of I to be maximized?

4. A shipload of 400 tourists, spending one day in port, may choose between three tours X, Y, and Z. Tours X and Y are limited to 150 persons each and tour Z to 100. Three hundred of the tourists assign preference points of 3, 2, and 1 respectively to tours X, Y, and Z; the remainder assign 1, 2, and 3 points to tours X, Y, and Z.

Delineate the allocation(s) of tourists to tours which will maximize the total of preference points.

5. A country imports 300 gallons of whiskey, 200 gallons of gin, and 150 gallons of vodka per week, which sell at $20, $10, and $40 respectively per gallon. At what levels should customs duties be levied on these spirits in order to maximize total revenue, given that the duty on any spirit may not exceed one-fifth of its wholesale price and that the total revenue collected from gin and vodka may not exceed that from whiskey? (Assume the quantities demanded are unaffected by the levels of duty.)

6. One-seventh of a 14-acre farm is suitable for potatoes (which return $3 per hundredweight), the remainder being suitable for wheat (returning $2 per bushel). Potatoes yield 20 hundredweight per acre, using 1 hour of labor per hundredweight, and wheat produces 10 bushels per acre, using $\frac{1}{2}$ hour of labor per bushel. Twenty hours of labor are available free, and up to 30 hours of casual labor may be hired at a cost of 20 cents per hour. If necessary the wheat land may be used for potatoes (but not vice versa); however, potatoes grown on this inferior soil return only $2.90 per hundredweight.

What is the maximum profit output mix on this farm, and how much casual labor should be hired?

16

THE DUAL AGAIN

16.1 Interpretation of Coefficients in Setting Up Primal and Dual Problems

At various points in previous chapters we have observed relationships between the primal and the dual forms of linear programming problems. It is now appropriate to consider some of these relationships in more detail. We first consider the precise meaning of each coefficient in both primal and dual forms of both maximization and minimization problems. For this purpose we continue to use as illustration our wheat/barley profit maximization problem and our feed-mix cost minimization problem, since these represent useful prototypes of the sorts of maximization and minimization problems encountered in practice.

16.1.1 Maximization Problems

At the end of Chapter 1 we stated our wheat/barley allocation problem in general terms as follows:

Maximize
$$z = c_1 x_1 + c_2 x_2 \tag{16.1a}$$

subject to
$$a_{11}x_1 + a_{12}x_2 \le b_1$$
$$a_{21}x_1 + a_{22}x_2 \le b_2 \tag{16.1b}$$
$$a_{31}x_1 + a_{32}x_2 \le b_3$$

and
$$x_1, x_2 \ge 0 \tag{16.1c}$$

where x_1 = number of bushels of wheat produced
x_2 = number of bushels of barley produced

In terms of our example, the coefficients in this statement of the problem are interpreted as follows:

a. Each c coefficient represents the money value (net profit, price) per unit of output. Thus c_1 represents the net return per bushel of wheat produced.

b. Each b coefficient represents the total supply of an input, expressed in whatever units are convenient. Thus b_2, for example, represents the number of man-hours of labor available.

c. Each a coefficient represents, in the same units as the corresponding b coefficient, the amount of a particular resource necessary to produce a unit of a particular product. Thus a_{32} measures the number of hundred-weight of fertilizer, (the third input) required to produce one bushel of barley (the second output).

Instead of two activities and three resources, as above, let us imagine a problem with n activities and m resources, with activities indexed by the subscript j ($j = 1, 2, \ldots, n$) and resources by the subscript i ($i = 1, 2, \ldots, m$). Then, in more general terms, the profit maximization problem may be written out, both symbolically and in longhand, as follows:

Maximize

$$
\begin{array}{ccccc}
z & = & \Sigma_j & c_j & \times & x_j \\
\begin{bmatrix} \text{Total} \\ \text{profit,} \\ \text{or total} \\ \text{money} \\ \text{value} \\ \text{of} \\ \text{outputs} \end{bmatrix} & equals & \begin{array}{l} \text{Sum} \\ \text{over} \\ \text{all } n \\ \text{outputs} \\ \text{of} \end{array} & \begin{bmatrix} \text{Profit,} \\ \text{or} \\ \text{money} \\ \text{value} \\ \text{per} \\ \text{unit of} \\ \text{output } j \end{bmatrix} & times & \begin{bmatrix} \text{Number} \\ \text{of} \\ \text{units} \\ \text{of} \\ \text{output } j \end{bmatrix}
\end{array} \qquad (16.2a)
$$

subject to, for each input i, ($i = 1, 2, \cdots, m$)

$$
\begin{array}{cccccc}
\Sigma_j & a_{ij} & \times & x_j & \leq & b_i \\
\begin{array}{l} \text{Sum} \\ \text{over} \\ \text{all } n \\ \text{outputs} \\ \text{of} \end{array} & \begin{bmatrix} \text{Number} \\ \text{of units} \\ \text{of} \\ \text{input } i \\ \text{required} \\ \text{per} \\ \text{unit of} \\ \text{output } j \end{bmatrix} & times & \begin{bmatrix} \text{Number} \\ \text{of units} \\ \text{of} \\ \text{output } j \end{bmatrix} & \begin{array}{l} must \\ be \\ equal \\ to\ or \\ less \\ than \end{array} & \begin{bmatrix} \text{Number} \\ \text{of units} \\ \text{of} \\ \text{input } i \\ \text{available} \end{bmatrix}
\end{array} \qquad (16.2b)
$$

and

$$
\begin{array}{ccc}
x_j & \geq & 0 \\
\begin{bmatrix} \text{Number} \\ \text{of units} \\ \text{of} \\ \text{output } j \end{bmatrix} & \begin{array}{l} must\ be \\ equal\ to \\ or\ greater \\ than \end{array} & \begin{bmatrix} \ \\ zero \\ \ \end{bmatrix}
\end{array} \qquad \begin{array}{l} (j = 1, 2, \cdots, n) \\[1em] (16.2c) \end{array}
$$

In Chapter 7 we observed how to write the dual of the particular primal problem in equation (16.1). Using exactly the same notation, *and placing exactly the same interpretation on each coefficient*, we set the dual problem up as follows:

Minimize

$$z' = b_1 u_1 + b_2 u_2 + b_3 u_3 \tag{16.3a}$$

subject to

$$a_{11} u_1 + a_{21} u_2 + a_{31} u_3 \geq c_1 \tag{16.3b}$$
$$a_{12} u_1 + a_{22} u_2 + a_{32} u_3 \geq c_2$$

and

$$u_1, u_2 \geq 0 \tag{16.3c}$$

where, as we have seen,

$u_1 =$ imputed money value per acre of land
$u_2 =$ imputed money value per man-hour of labor
$u_3 =$ imputed money value per cwt. of fertilizer.

We may therefore write the dual of the profit maximization problem in general terms as follows:

Minimize

z'	=	Σ_i	b_i	×	u_i	
$\begin{bmatrix} \text{Total} \\ \text{money} \\ \text{value} \\ \text{of} \\ \text{inputs} \end{bmatrix}$	*equals*	$\begin{array}{l} \text{Sum} \\ \text{over} \\ \text{all } m \\ \text{inputs} \\ \text{of} \end{array}$	$\begin{bmatrix} \text{Number} \\ \text{of units} \\ \text{of} \\ \text{input } i \\ \text{available} \end{bmatrix}$	*times*	$\begin{bmatrix} \text{Imputed} \\ \text{money} \\ \text{value} \\ \text{per} \\ \text{unit of} \\ \text{input } i \end{bmatrix}$	(16.4a)

subject to, for each output j $(j = 1, 2, \cdots, n)$

Σ_i	a_{ij}	×	u_i	$\geq$	c_j	
$\begin{array}{l} \text{Sum} \\ \text{over} \\ \text{all} \\ \text{inputs} \\ \text{of} \end{array}$	$\begin{bmatrix} \text{Number} \\ \text{of units} \\ \text{of} \\ \text{input } i \\ \text{required} \\ \text{per} \\ \text{unit of} \\ \text{output } j \end{bmatrix}$	*times*	$\begin{bmatrix} \text{Imputed} \\ \text{money} \\ \text{value} \\ \text{per} \\ \text{unit of} \\ \text{input } i \end{bmatrix}$	$\begin{array}{l} \textit{must} \\ \textit{be} \\ \textit{equal} \\ \textit{to or} \\ \textit{greater} \\ \textit{than} \end{array}$	$\begin{bmatrix} \text{Profit,} \\ \text{or} \\ \text{money} \\ \text{value} \\ \text{per} \\ \text{unit of} \\ \text{output } j \end{bmatrix}$	(16.4b)

and

$$
\begin{array}{ccc}
u_i & \geq & 0 \qquad (i = 1, 2, \cdots, m) \\
\begin{bmatrix} \text{Imputed} \\ \text{money} \\ \text{value per} \\ \text{unit of} \\ \text{input } i \end{bmatrix} & \begin{array}{l} must\ be \\ equal\ to \\ or\ greater \\ than \end{array} & \begin{bmatrix} \ \\ \text{zero} \\ \ \end{bmatrix}
\end{array}
\qquad (16.4c)
$$

By comparing equation (16.2a) with equation (16.4a) we can see clearly how in the primal the problem is to solve for the optimal output mix, whereas in the dual the aim is to solve for the values to be imputed to each of the inputs. In the primal objective function, equation (16.2a), the data consist of *per unit* profits, or money values, (c_j), for the outputs, whereas in the objective function of the dual, equation (16.4a), the data consist of the *total* supplies (b_i) of inputs. Thus, overall, in both objective functions we are summing money values per unit *times* number of units (of outputs in the primal, of inputs in the dual); as we have seen, at the optimum solution for the x's and the u's, the total money value of outputs (z) equals the total money value of inputs (z').

This comparison may be carried on into the interpretation of the constraints in equations (16.2b) and (16.4b). In the primal, where we aim at selecting *total* outputs (x_j) of the activities, we are constrained through the input-output coefficients (a_{ij}) not to exceed *total* supplies (b_i) of inputs. On the other hand, in the dual, where the exercise is to determine *per unit* imputed money values (u_i) of the inputs, we are constrained, through the same input-output coefficients (a_{ij}), not to fall short of *per unit* profits, or money values, (c_j) of the outputs.

16.1.2 Minimization Problems

The cornmeal/fishmeal feed-mix example is stated in formal terms as

Minimize

$$ z = c_1 x_1 + c_2 x_2 \qquad (16.5a) $$

subject to

$$
\begin{aligned}
a_{11}x_1 + a_{12}x_2 &\geq b_1 \\
a_{21}x_1 + a_{22}x_2 &\geq b_2 \\
a_{31}x_1 + a_{32}x_2 &\geq b_3
\end{aligned}
\qquad (16.5b)
$$

and

$$ x_1, x_2 \geq 0 \qquad (16.5c) $$

where x_1 = number of tons of cornmeal used
x_2 = number of tons of fishmeal used

The interpretation of coefficients is as follows:

a. Each c coefficient represents the money value (net cost) per unit of raw material. Thus c_2, for example, represents the net cost in dollars of a ton of fishmeal.

b. Each b coefficient represents the total specified requirement of an ingredient, expressed in whatever units are convenient. Thus b_3 represents the number of units of fiber required in the final mix.

c. Each a coefficient represents, in the same units as the corresponding b coefficient, the ingredient content per unit of a particular raw material. Thus a_{12}, for instance, refers to the number of units of protein (the first of the required ingredients) contained in each ton of fishmeal (the second of the raw materials).

Now, let us set up the minimization problem in more general terms for n raw materials and m ingredient specifications, where the raw materials are indexed by the subscript j $(j = 1, 2, \cdots, n)$ and the ingredients by the subscript i $(i = 1, 2, \cdots, m)$.

To point up the general symmetry, in economic terms, between this prototype minimization problem and the maximization problems of the sort considered in the previous section, let us substitute "input" for "raw material," and "output" for "ingredient." Thus we can speak of certain combinations of inputs, i.e., cornmeal and fishmeal in our example, producing certain outputs of protein, oil, and fiber in a final mixture.

The problem is set up as follows:

Minimize

$$
\underset{\begin{bmatrix} \text{Total} \\ \text{cost,} \\ \text{or total} \\ \text{money} \\ \text{value} \\ \text{of} \\ \text{inputs} \end{bmatrix}}{z}
\underset{equals}{=}
\underset{\begin{matrix} \text{Sum} \\ \text{over} \\ \text{all } n \\ \text{inputs} \\ \text{of} \end{matrix}}{\Sigma_j}
\underset{\begin{bmatrix} \text{Cost, or} \\ \text{money} \\ \text{value} \\ \text{per} \\ \text{unit of} \\ \text{input } j \end{bmatrix}}{c_j}
\underset{times}{\times}
\underset{\begin{bmatrix} \text{Number} \\ \text{of units} \\ \text{of} \\ \text{input } j \end{bmatrix}}{x_j}
\qquad (16.6a)
$$

subject to, for each output i, $(i = 1, 2, \cdots, m)$

$$
\underset{\begin{matrix} \text{Sum} \\ \text{over} \\ \text{all } n \\ \text{inputs} \\ \text{of} \end{matrix}}{\Sigma_j}
\underset{\begin{bmatrix} \text{Number} \\ \text{of units} \\ \text{of} \\ \text{output } i \\ \text{supplied} \\ \text{per} \\ \text{unit of} \\ \text{input } j \end{bmatrix}}{a_{ij}}
\underset{times}{\times}
\underset{\begin{bmatrix} \text{Number} \\ \text{of units} \\ \text{of} \\ \text{input } j \end{bmatrix}}{x_j}
\underset{\begin{matrix} \textit{must be} \\ \textit{equal} \\ \textit{to or} \\ \textit{greater} \\ \textit{than} \end{matrix}}{\geq}
\underset{\begin{bmatrix} \text{Number} \\ \text{of units} \\ \text{of} \\ \text{output } i \\ \text{required} \end{bmatrix}}{b_i}
\qquad (16.6b)
$$

and

$$x_j \qquad \geq \qquad 0 \qquad\qquad (j = 1, 2, \cdots, n)$$

$$\begin{bmatrix} \text{Number} \\ \text{of units} \\ \text{of} \\ \text{input } j \end{bmatrix} \begin{array}{l} \textit{must be} \\ \textit{equal to} \\ \textit{or greater} \\ \textit{than} \end{array} \begin{bmatrix} \text{zero} \\ \\ \\ \end{bmatrix} \qquad\qquad (16.6c)$$

The dual of this initial minimization problem may be set up as follows, using exactly the same notation as above, and, as in the maximization example, *placing exactly the same interpretation on each coefficient.*

Maximize

$$z' = b_1 u_1 + b_2 u_2 + b_3 u_3 \qquad\qquad (16.7a)$$

subject to

$$a_{11}u_1 + a_{21}u_2 + a_{31}u_3 \leq c_1 \qquad\qquad (16.7b)$$
$$a_{12}u_1 + a_{22}u_2 + a_{32}u_3 \leq c_2$$

and

$$u_1, u_2, u_3 \geq 0 \qquad\qquad (16.7c)$$

where, as we have seen,

$u_1 =$ imputed money value per unit of protein
$u_2 =$ imputed money value per unit of oil
$u_3 =$ imputed money value per unit of fiber

In general terms the dual of the cost minimization problem is written as follows:

Maximize

$$z' \qquad = \qquad \Sigma_i \qquad b_i \qquad \times \qquad u_i$$

$$\begin{bmatrix} \text{Total} \\ \text{money} \\ \text{value} \\ \text{of} \\ \text{outputs} \end{bmatrix} \begin{array}{l} \textit{equals} \end{array} \begin{array}{l} \text{Sum} \\ \text{over} \\ \text{all } m \\ \text{outputs} \\ \text{of} \end{array} \begin{bmatrix} \text{Number} \\ \text{of units} \\ \text{of} \\ \text{output } i \\ \text{required} \end{bmatrix} \begin{array}{l} \textit{times} \end{array} \begin{bmatrix} \text{Imputed} \\ \text{money} \\ \text{value per} \\ \text{unit of} \\ \text{output } i \end{bmatrix} \qquad (16.8a)$$

subject to, for each input j $(j = 1, 2, \cdots, n)$

$$\Sigma_i \qquad a_{ij} \qquad \times \qquad u_i \qquad \leq \qquad c_j$$

$$\begin{array}{l} \text{Sum} \\ \text{over} \\ \text{all } m \\ \text{outputs} \\ \text{of} \end{array} \begin{bmatrix} \text{Number} \\ \text{of units} \\ \text{of} \\ \text{output } i \\ \text{supplied} \\ \text{per} \\ \text{unit of} \\ \text{input } j \end{bmatrix} \begin{array}{l} \textit{times} \end{array} \begin{bmatrix} \text{Imputed} \\ \text{money} \\ \text{value} \\ \text{per} \\ \text{unit of} \\ \text{output } i \end{bmatrix} \begin{array}{l} \textit{must be} \\ \textit{equal to} \\ \textit{or less} \\ \textit{than} \end{array} \begin{bmatrix} \text{Cost, or} \\ \text{money} \\ \text{value} \\ \text{per} \\ \text{unit of} \\ \text{input } j \end{bmatrix} \qquad (16.8b)$$

and

$$u_i \qquad \geq \qquad 0 \qquad (i = 1, 2, \cdots, m)$$

$$\begin{bmatrix} \text{Imputed} \\ \text{money} \\ \text{value per} \\ \text{unit of} \\ \text{output } i \end{bmatrix} \quad \begin{matrix} must\ be \\ equal\ to \\ or\ greater \\ than \end{matrix} \quad \begin{bmatrix} \\ \\ \text{zero} \\ \\ \end{bmatrix} \qquad (16.8c)$$

As with the initial maximization problem we may compare primal and dual. We observe again that the objective function of the primal, equation (16.6a), sets out to determine *total* levels (x_j) of inputs, whereas the aim of the dual is to find *per unit* money values (u_i) of the outputs. Similarly, data in the primal are *per unit* costs, or money values, (c_j) of the n inputs, while in the dual, *total* requirements (b_i) of the m outputs are given. Hence, again, we attempt in both primal and dual to maximize the sum of money values per unit *times* number of units (of input in the primal and output in the dual). Again, as we know, the total values, z and z', are identical for the optimal sets of x's and u's.

In both the present section and the previous one the correspondence between primal and dual has been observed. We may also compare the correspondence between the two sections themselves, i.e., between the profit maximization problem of section 16.1.1 and the cost minimization problem of section 16.1.2. By using the terms "input" and "output" in both expositions, and by letting "money value" denote both "profit" and "cost," we have made possible a direct comparison between the statements of the primal problems in equations (16.2) and (16.6) and also between the dual problems in equations (16.4) and (16.8). The reader should himself compare these sets of statements and observe the symmetry between them, referring to the earlier discussions of the transformation of maximization problems to minimization and vice versa (section 6.1), and of the transformation of maximum to minimum constraints and vice versa (section 8.4.3).

16.2 Symmetry of Primal and Dual Problems During Solution

To illustrate the relationships between primal and dual solution sequences for a given problem, the dual of the feed-mix example is solved in this section, both graphically and by use of the simplex. This solution sequence is compared with the graphical and the simplex solutions of the primal form of the problem as shown in Chapters 2 and 14.

TABLE 16.1

Tableau 1

| | Real Variables | | | Slack Variables | | | |
	Protein Value u_1	Oil Value u_2	Fiber Value u_3	Cornmeal Value s_1^*	Fishmeal Value s_2^*	b	R
$z - c$ row	-4	-6	-14	0	0	0	
s_1^* Slack cornmeal value	1	1	$\circled{7}$	1	0	3	$3/7$ ←
s_2^* Slack fishmeal value	1	3	0	0	1	5	—

Tableau 2

	u_1	u_2	u_3	s_1^*	s_2^*	b	R
$z - c$ row	-2	-4	0	2	0	6	
u_3 Fiber value	$1/7$	$1/7$	1	$1/7$	0	$3/7$	3
s_2^* Slack fishmeal value	1	$\circled{3}$	0	0	1	5	$5/3$ ←

Tableau 3

u_1	u_2	u_3	s^*	s_2^*	b		R
$-2/3$	0	0	2	$4/3$	$12\,2/3$	$z - c$ row	
(2/21)	0	1	$1/7$	$-1/21$	$4/21$	u_3 Fiber value	$2\leftarrow$ / 5
$1/3$	1	0	0	$1/3$	$5/3$	u_2 Oil value	

←

Tableau 4

u_1	u_2	u_3	s_1^*	s_2^*	b	
0	0	7	3	1	14	$z - c$ row
1	0	$10\,1/2$	$11\,1/2$	$-1/2$	2	u_1 Protein value
0	1	$-3\,1/2$	$-1/2$	$1/2$	1	u_2 Oil value

16.2.1   Solution of the Dual Feed-Mix Problem

The dual of the feed-mix problem is written numerically as follows: Determine imputed money values per unit for protein, oil, and fiber, u_1, u_2, and u_3 respectively, which maximize

$$z' = 4u_1 + 6u_2 + 14u_3 \qquad (16.9a)$$

subject to

$$1u_1 + 1u_2 + 7u_3 \leq 3 \text{ (cornmeal value)}$$
$$1u_1 + 3u_2 \qquad \leq 5 \text{ (fishmeal value)} \qquad (16.9b)$$

and

$$u_1, u_2, u_3 \geq 0 \qquad (16.9c)$$

Since the inequations in (16.9b) constrain the total imputed values of ingredients with respect to each raw material unit value, we can in turn define slack variables in terms of raw material unit values. Thus, let s_1^* and s_2^* represent "slack cornmeal unit value" and "slack fishmeal unit value" and add them to the constraints in (16.9b) in the usual way.[1] This yields the set of equations

$$1u_1 + 1u_2 + 7u_3 + 1s_1^* \qquad = 3 \qquad (16.10)$$
$$1u_1 + 3u_2 \qquad + 1s_2^* = 5$$

The simplex solution of this simple maximization problem is given in Table 16.1. The mechanical calculations are straightforward and need not be discussed, but some coefficients need interpretation.

In the preceding discussion we have observed that:

In the primal we select *total levels* of variables (real, slack, and/or surplus), given certain *unit values* as parameters; whereas in the dual we select *unit values* (for real, slack, and/or surplus variables), given certain *total levels* of variables as data.

This statement may be rephrased as follows:

In the primal the levels of *basic* variables, as given in the b column, measure *total levels* of real, slack, and/or surplus variables, and the valuations imputed to *nonbasic* variables as given in the $z - c$ row measure *unit values*; whereas in the dual the levels of basic variables as given in the b column measure *unit values* of real, slack, and/or surplus variables, and the imputed values of *nonbasic* variables as given in the $z - c$ row measure *total levels* of these variables.

Look at Tableaux 1 and 4 of Table 16.1 as an illustration. In Tableau 1, the basic variables are s_1^* and s_2^*; their b-column values show that slack

---

[1] The notation "$s*$" is used in order to distinguish these slack variables from the surplus variables "s" already defined for the primal form of this problem.

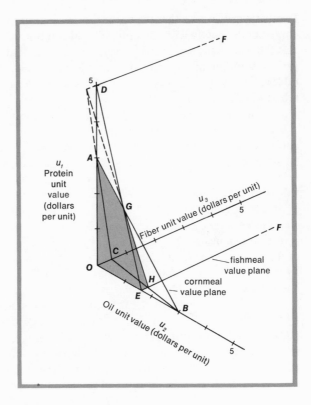

Figure 16.1

cornmeal value enters the solution at a level of $3 *per ton*, and slack fishmeal value at a level of $5 *per ton*. The nonbasic variables are u_1, u_2, and u_3; their $z - c$-row values show *total* specifications of protein, oil, and fiber of 4, 6, and 14 units respectively.[2] Again, in Tableau 4, the basic variables u_1 and u_2 measure money values *per unit* of protein and oil ($2 per unit and $1 per unit respectively), while the $z - c$-row elements for the nonbasic variables measure *total levels*: 7 units of surplus fiber, 3 tons of cornmeal, and 1 ton of fishmeal.

The optimal set of valuations of the three ingredients is yielded by the final tableau of Table 16.1. We see that the optimal imputed value of protein is $2 per unit (measured by u_1), that of oil is $1 per unit ($u_2$), and that of fiber is $0 per unit (since u_3 is nonbasic and therefore zero). This solution tallies with the dual solution read from the optimal primal tableau, shown as Tableau 5 of Table 14.1. In that tableau we observe the $z - c$-row values of s_1 and s_2, the surplus variables for the fully met protein and oil specifications to be $2 per unit and $1 per unit respectively.

[2] A discussion of signs comes later; at present we wish only to observe the units of measurement.

In other words we see that the optimal primal solution of the dual problem corresponds exactly with the optimal dual solution of the primal problem.

Again, as expected, the dual solution of the dual corresponds to the primal solution of the primal; i.e., the $z - c$ row of the optimal dual tableau in Table 16.1 tallies with the b column of the optimal primal tableau in Table 14.1, specifying 3 tons of cornmeal, 1 ton of fishmeal, and 7 units of surplus fiber as the optimum combination.

This solution is confirmed graphically in Figure 16.1. This diagram, constructed in the familiar manner, can be viewed as if the u_2 and the u_3 axes are in the horizontal plane, with the u_1 axis rising vertically from the origin. The two-dimensional plane ACB shows the upper limits on the values of u_1, u_2, and u_3 placed by the unit value of cornmeal; this plane is drawn bounded by CB, BA, and AC representing the nonnegativity condition on u_1, u_3, and u_2 respectively. Similarly the constraint imposed by the unit value of fishmeal is shown by the plane OEF, which lies parallel to the u_3 axis, meeting it at infinity (F). This plane is also shown bounded by the nonnegativity conditions for u_1, u_2, and u_3 represented by EF, DF, and DE respectively. The two planes in the figure intersect along GH, and hence the feasible region is the three-dimensional shaded area $OCAGEH$.

It is difficult, without overcomplicating the figure, to draw the "profit plane" onto Figure 16.1. The reader will gain an idea of its configuration if he sketches in the plane formed by joining, say, the points on the axes where $u_1 = 7$, $u_2 = 4\frac{2}{3}$, and $u_3 = 2$. (Why these points?) He will then see that its slope is such that the optimal solution lies at point G, where $u_3 = 0$.

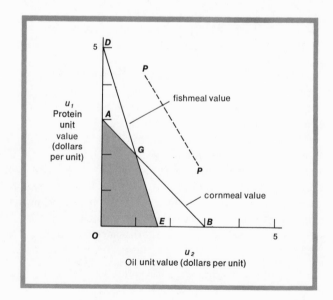

Figure 16.2

Knowing this, a more accurate graphical reading of the optimum can be obtained by redrawing the figure in two dimensions in the plane of the u_1 and u_2 axes only. This is shown in Figure 16.2, in which the lettering is taken direct from Figure 16.1. We find that the optimum solution for this problem is $u_1 = 2$ (dollars per unit of protein), $u_2 = 1$ (dollar per unit of oil), and $u_3 = 0$ (dollars per unit of fiber), confirming the simplex solution above.

16.2.2 Comparison of the Dual Solution Sequence with the Primal

The sequences of bases through which the primal and the dual simplex solutions of the feed-mix problem pass are summarized in Table 16.2. The $z - c$-row values of nonbasic variables at each tableau are also listed. Remember that artificial variables were used in the simplex solution of the original primal minimization problem; these have no interest other than as a computational device, hence we give in Table 16.2 the *actual* values of the surplus variables in the solution to that problem. In Tableaux 1 through 3 in this construction, one or more surplus variables are negative and therefore the primal solution is infeasible.

TABLE 16.2

	Minimization (Primal) Form				Maximization (Dual) Form		
Tableau	Primal Solution	Dual Solution	Point on Fig. 14.1	Tableau	Primal Solution	Dual Solution	Point on Fig. 16.1
1.	$s_1 = -4$ $s_2 = -6$ $s_3 = -14$ *infeasible*	$x_1 = 3$ $x_2 = 5$ *feasible*	O	1.	$s_1^* = 3$ $s^* = 5$ *feasible*	$u_1 = -4$ $u_2 = -6$ $u_3 = -14$ *infeasible*	O
2.	$s_1 = -2$ $s_2 = -4$ $x_1 = 2$ *infeasible*	$x_2 = 5$ $s_3 = \frac{3}{7}$ *feasible*	F	2.	$s_2^* = 5$ $u_3 = \frac{3}{7}$ *feasible*	$u_1 = -2$ $u_2 = -4$ $s_1^* = 2$ *infeasible*	C
3.	$s_1 = -\frac{2}{3}$ $x_1 = 2$ $x_2 = 11\frac{1}{3}$ *infeasible*	$s_2 = 1\frac{2}{3}$ $s_3 = \frac{4}{21}$ *feasible*	J	3.	$u_2 = 1\frac{2}{3}$ $u_3 = \frac{4}{21}$ *feasible*	$u_1 = -\frac{2}{3}$ $s_1^* = 2$ $s_2^* = 11\frac{1}{3}$ *infeasible*	H
4.	$s_2 = 2$ $x_1 = 2$ $x_2 = 2$ *feasible*	$s_1 = 5$ $s_3 = -\frac{2}{7}$ *infeasible*	H				
5.	$s_3 = 7$ $x_1 = 3$ $x_2 = 1$ *feasible*	$s_1 = 2$ $s_2 = 1$ *feasible*	E	4.	$u_1 = 2$ $u_2 = 1$ *feasible*	$u_3 = 7$ $s_1^* = 3$ $s^* = 1$ *feasible*	G

231

A dual solution is also "infeasible" when it contains negative values, since it directly implies that one or more of the dual variables are negative, thus violating one or more of the nonnegativity conditions. This is best illustrated by Tableau 4 of the solution to the minimization form. But before referring to this tableau, let us establish the correspondence between the previous tableaux in each solution sequence. As we mentioned above, the variables s_1, s_2, and s_3 in the primal minimization form correspond directly to the variables u_1, u_2, and u_3 in the dual maximization form, and likewise the variables x_1 and x_2 are identical with the variables s_1^* and s_2^*. We see therefore that Tableaux 1, 2, and 3 of the solution sequence for the primal (minimization) problem happen to correspond exactly with Tableaux 1, 2, and 3 of the solution sequence for the dual (maximization) problem. These solutions are identical in all respects, and if the full matrixes in Tables 14.1 and 16.1 are compared for these tableaux, we find that all coefficients are identical in absolute values, except of course that they are transposed; i.e., rows have become columns and columns rows. It is further apparent that there is no difference between, say, point C on Figure 16.1 and point F on Figure 14.1; they are simply different pictorial representations of the same overall set of values for primal and dual variables.

We have said "happen to correspond" in the previous paragraph because there is no necessary reason why the primal and the dual solution sequences should follow exactly the same path in reaching an optimum. Indeed in our example the solution paths diverge after Tableau 3. This brings us back to the question of the infeasible dual solution in Tableau 4 of Table 14.1. This tableau represents the nonoptimal point H on Figure 14.1; a further iteration leads to the optimum vertex E. In the maximization problem, on the other hand, the simplex moves direct from point H on Figure 16.1 to the optimum point, G.

Of course we could have derived Tableau 5 directly from Tableau 3 in Table 14.1 (i.e., moved direct from J to E on Figure 14.1) by disobeying rule 1D of the simplex and introducing s_3 to replace s_1', pivoting on the coefficient $\frac{2}{21}$. Alternatively we can illustrate the movement to point E through point H on Figure 14.1 by reconstructing this path in the solution to the dual (minimization) problem as follows. Taking Tableau 3 of Table 16.1, we may disobey the simplex rule 2B and introduce u_1, replacing u_2 instead of u_3 pivoting on the coefficient $\frac{1}{3}$. The reader may himself perform this calculation, observing that the resultant matrix corresponds to Tableau 4 of Table 14.1. The basic solution resulting from this transformation is $u_1 = 5$, $u_3 = -\frac{2}{7}$; in terms of Figure 16.1 it means that in moving up HG from H, G is actually by-passed (disobedience of rule 2B), and the solution moves on to point J, where $u_1 = 5$, $u_3 = -\frac{2}{7}$, a point clearly infeasible with respect to the u_3 nonnegativity condition.

Hence we have seen, as suggested earlier, that a "dual solution" (as shown by the $z - c$ row of any tableau) is infeasible when it contains negative elements, since it implies infeasible values of the dual variables. Thus the dual solution of Tableau 4 in Table 14.1 is infeasible because it implies an infeasible value of the dual variable u_3.

In summary, in this section we have seen how the primal and the dual forms of a given problem contain absolutely identical information, being simply different ways of writing the same problem. This is true for any tableau: each vertex of the constraint set of the primal problem implies a corresponding vertex on the constraint set of the dual problem, and vice versa. Hence any set of values of the primal variables obtained during the solution of a problem implies a corresponding set of values of the dual variables, and vice versa.

16.3 Feasible/Infeasible Solutions in Primal/Dual Problems

An important theorem of linear programming, the proof of which does not concern us here, states that if a solution to a problem is feasible with respect to both primal and dual variables, that solution is optimal. If the optimal solution is unique (no degeneracy; see section 9.6.2), just one combination of primal and dual variables is feasible; all other combinations of variables will contain at least one primal or dual variable which is infeasible (negative).

To illustrate, look at Table 16.2. In Tableaux 1, 2, and 3 we see that while the dual solution of the primal problem (and hence the primal solution of the dual) is feasible, the primal solution of the primal problem (and hence the dual solution of the dual) is infeasible, containing negative values. In Tableau 4 of the minimization form the primal solution at last becomes feasible, but (as we have noted earlier) the dual becomes infeasible, and hence the solution represented by this tableau is nonoptimal. In Tableau 5 of the minimization form (and correspondingly Tableau 4 of the maximization form) both primal and dual solutions are feasible, and the overall solution is optimal.

While we shall not rigorously prove this theorem, we can at least demonstrate that moving away from the optimal point in our example, in whichever way we choose to move, will cause one or more primal or dual variables to become infeasible.

Look at Figure 14.1, where the optimum vertex is E. If we move away from E to A or to J, say, the primal solution clearly becomes infeasible, since such movements lead us straight into the infeasible region as originally defined. A movement to C or to H, on the other hand, leaves the primal solution feasible, since it is simply moving along a boundary of the feasible region. However, in these latter cases, the *dual* becomes infeasible. Why?

Because a movement from E to C in Figure 14.1 is, as we know, equivalent to introducing s_1 into the basis at E (Tableau 5, Table 14.1), replacing x_2. In terms of the dual calculation, this is absolutely identical to introducing s_2^* into the optimal basis (Tableau 4, Table 16.1) and eliminating u_1, leading to a new basis containing $s_2^* = -4$ and $u_2 = 3$ (the reader may confirm the calculations). This basis is clearly infeasible. In terms of Figure 16.1 the infeasibility of this movement is verified by observing that it corresponds to a shift from G to B, a movement into the infeasible region. Thus, in an *ad hoc* manner it has been demonstrated that moving in any direction from the optimal vertex, where both primal and dual solutions are feasible, will cause one or more primal or dual variables to become infeasible.

The reader may, as an exercise, reaffirm the above argument from the other angle, i.e., by showing that a movement from G to, say, E or H or A in Figure 16.1, while feasible with respect to the dual variables u_1, u_2, and u_3, would produce infeasible values for the primal variables x_1 and x_2.

The implications of these results for the economic interpretation of linear programming models can now be summarized as follows. Let us talk in terms of a profit maximization model, though as the reader should easily appreciate, similar arguments apply to minimization applications. For whatever situation a particular model is set up, a given formulation will lead to just one set of levels of outputs and one set of price imputations for resources which will optimize the objective of the system.[3] Alternatively this may be stated as follows: Any given linear programming formulation implies a single equilibrium output mix and a single set of equilibrium prices. As we saw in the case of the original dual example in Chapter 7, this result accords with the perfect competition model in long-run equilibrium. Similarly if we formulate a linear programming model of a whole economy instead of a single firm, the same result holds: we determine a single optimal mixture of outputs for the system together with a single equilibrium set of factor prices.

16.4 Stability of Shadow-Price Estimates

In our profit maximization examples we have seen how the dual solution yields estimates of the marginal value productivity of those resources which in the optimal solution are fully utilized. This tells us how much more or less profit could be earned if one extra or fewer unit of each resource were available, other things remaining constant. In minimization problems, also, the dual solution provides us with similar information about the movement in total costs if a particular requirement specification is changed by one unit, other things again being equal.

[3] This assumes that a primal/dual feasible solution *exists*.

It is important to understand that other things may not be equal. In particular, changing the availability of a resource by one (or more, or less) unit or altering a minimum requirement by one (or more, or less) unit may change the whole structure of an optimal solution.

This may be illustrated by the feed-mix example. In Figure 14.1 the optimal solution is at E, where $x_1 = 3$ tons cornmeal and $x_2 = 1$ ton fishmeal. The optimal dual solution shows that the shadow price for protein, given by the $z - c$-row coefficient for the variable s_1 in Tableau 5 of Table 14.1, is $2 per unit. Thus, increasing the protein requirement in a mixture by 1 unit will increase total costs by $2, moving them from $14 to $16. This can be demonstrated graphically. An increase in protein requirement from 4 to 5 units would move the line AB in Figure 14.1 outward. Its new position will be $A'B'$, as shown in Figure 16.3; the new optimal point will be at E', where $x_1 = 4\frac{1}{2}$ tons and $x_2 = \frac{1}{2}$ ton. The total cost of this mixture, optimum for a protein requirement of 5 units, is ($4\frac{1}{2}$ tons cornmeal *times* $3 per ton) *plus* ($\frac{1}{2}$ ton fishmeal *times* $5 per ton) *equals* $16, as expected. It is apparent that the same situation would obtain if the protein specification were increased by one further unit, from 5 to 6 units. The optimum would move to C, and total costs would increase by a further $2 to $18. That is, at point E' in Figure 16.3, the shadow price of protein would still be $2 per unit, just as it was at E in Figure 14.1.

Let us now consider *reducing* the protein requirement from its original level of 4 units. The original dual solution still indicates that reducing the protein requirement should reduce total costs by $2 per unit of protein, i.e., from $14 to $12. Performing this reduction graphically yields a new constraint $A''B''$, as shown in Figure 16.4. The new optimal solution lies

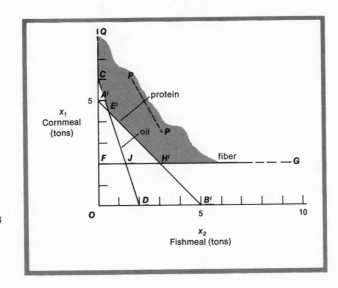

Figure 16.3

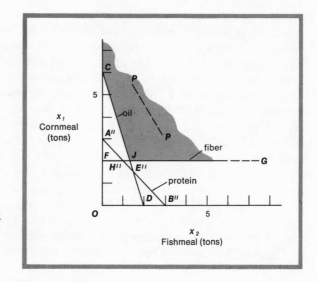

Figure 16.4

at J, where $x_1 = 2$ tons, $x_2 = 1\frac{1}{3}$ tons, and total costs $= \$12\frac{2}{3}$, not $\$12$ as expected.

The explanation is obvious. In moving the constraint AB inward from its original position, we have passed another vertex, J, and the structure of the whole solution has changed. In fact, in its new position at $A''B''$ (protein requirement 3 units), a zero shadow price is indicated for protein, since any small variation in protein requirement from 3 units will have no effect on the optimum at J.

It is clear from the above discussion that a particular shadow price may be regarded as stable only with respect to variations in resource supply or in requirements that do not cause the optimal solution to reach a new vertex[4] (defining a "new vertex" as one formed by a different set of constraints from that forming the original optimum vertex). Dissecting the downward movement of the constraint AB in Figure 14.1, we can see that the shadow price of protein will stay at $\$2$ per unit, whenever the point of intersection of AB and CD lies above point J. When these two points coincide, the shadow price of protein will fall to zero, as we saw originally in our discussion of degenerate solutions in section 9.4 (see especially Figure 9.6). Further movement of the constraint downward from this position (toward and beyond $A''B''$ in Figure 16.4) will not alter the zero shadow price of protein any further.

The conclusion to be drawn from this discussion is that when considering shifts in resource availability or requirement specifications, shadow-price information as yielded by an optimal dual solution must be

[4] Strictly, this statement applies only to unique optimal solutions.

interpreted with caution. This question will be taken up in more detail in the next volume; meanwhile it should be borne in mind that, in the absence of specific calculations on the stability of shadow-price estimates, these values must be regarded as applying to small changes only.

EXERCISES

1. Referring to exercise 4 in Chapter 8, suppose a pair of trousers returns \$5 and a suit \$11. Set up the dual of this profit maximization problem. What do the dual variables measure? Explain the interpretation of all coefficients.
2. Solve the problem in exercise 1. Compare your solution sequence with that of the primal (refer to the graph in exercise 5 of Chapter 8, and to the simplex solution in exercise 5 of Chapter 13).
3. Write the dual form of the diet problem in the exercises of Chapter 10. What do the dual variables measure? Explain the interpretation of all coefficients.
4. Solve the problem in exercise 3. Compare your solution sequence with the graphical and simplex solutions to the primal problem found in the exercises of Chapter 10.
5. Take the wheat/barley profit maximization example of Chapter 1 (see equation [1.12]). We have found that the shadow price of land in this problem is \$2 per acre (see Table 13.1, Tableau 3). Over what range of land supply (i.e., above and below its present level of 8 acres) will this shadow price remain at \$2?
6. In Exercise 5, what would be the effect on the shadow price of land if the price of barley rose from \$6 to \$7?

INDEX